14 Days

W9-AYP-551

Men and Women Behind the Atom

by SARAH R. RIEDMAN
Illustrated

There have been a number of books for teen-agers about the release of atomic energy, but nothing about the people responsible for it. Dr. Riedman has now presented us with a book about a number of the men and women who played a part in this world-shaking discovery. She tells us about their childhood, their family environment, and their development into men and women. She also discusses the discoveries and research of all of them, carefully explaining all her scientific terms. Now, for the first time, young people can understand how many years of research went into the making of the bomb, and what the peace-time uses of atomic energy will be, in the human terms of the people behind the scene.

Here is the table of contents:

Atomic Honeycomb: technician inserting fuel rod into Preliminary Pile Assembly at Knolls Atomic Power Laboratory. The reactor is the first to be operated in the north-eastern United States.

MEN AND WOMEN BEHIND THE ATOM

SARAH R. RIEDMAN

ILLUSTRATED WITH PHOTOGRAPHS

ABELARD-SCHUMAN

London   New York   Toronto

DEDICATION

To the men and women

whose knowledge and self-sacrifice

have opened the enormous possibilities

for peace and plenty for all mankind

TABLE OF CONTENTS

LIST OF ILLUSTRATIONS

ACKNOWLEDGMENTS

To all those whose works make up the rich stores that I have tapped for source material, I wish to give most grateful acknowledgment. Without these this book, an effort which may hopefully be justified if it makes these works more available to the young reader, could not have been written. The reader whose interest leads him to search for additional information will find it in the books and articles listed in the appended bibliography.

Special thanks are due to Professor Aage Bohr who generously furnished textual and photographic material for the chapter on Niels Bohr, to Dr P. Biquard for his courtesy in supplying a biographical source on Joliot-Curie, to Eve Curie Labouisse and her secretary Mrs. Dagmar Keller for most generous help in securing and kind permission to reproduce the photographs from Eve Curie's book, *Madame Curie* (facing pages 32, 33, 40, 41, 56, 57), to Mr. Hugo Gernsback, publisher of *Electrical Experimenter,* for material and illustrations from that journal (facing page 17).

For additional photographic material the author owes acknowledgment to: French Embassy Press and Information Division for pictures on facing pages 16 and 152; British Information Services for pictures on facing pages 73, 89, 104, 105, 216 and 217; Wide World Photos for pictures on facing pages 88 and 201; The University of Chicago Press for pictures on facing pages 153, 168 and 169; from *Atoms in the Family* by Laura Fermi (Copyright 1954 by the University of Chicago); Oxford University Press, Inc. for pictures on facing pages 184, 185 and 200; from *Atomic Quest* by Arthur Holly Compton (Copyright 1956 by Oxford University Press, Inc.); News Bureau of General Electric Co., for the frontispiece.

S.R.R.

ATOM
HEADLINES
AND
PEOPLE

On October 17, 1956, Queen Elizabeth II threw the switch that put into operation the first full-scale atomic power station in the world. The twin reactors at Calder Hall, Cumberland, England, are capable of producing 75,000 kilowatts an hour, enough to supply all the electrical needs of about 500,000 people. It takes eleven tons of coal to generate this amount of electricity. At Calder Hall it takes only a little more than a tenth of an ounce of atomic 'fuel' – *uranium*.

The U.S. Navy's submarine *Nautilus*, launched on January 17, 1955, traveled 60,000 miles – about two and a half times the distance around the earth – on a chunk of uranium the size of a golf ball. Had it used oil, the two-year trip would have burned up 720,000 gallons, the capacity of 90 railway tank cars.

The bomb that wiped out the city of Hiroshima on August 6, 1945, had the power of 20,000 *tons* of TNT. Just how much *atomic* explosive was required is still a secret, but it undoubtedly could be measured in pounds and ounces.

Yet these astounding events are the merest beginnings of man's eventual utilization of the nearly inexhaustible energy locked in the atom.

THE POSSIBILITIES for tapping these untold resources opened up on December 2, 1942. For the first time, on that historic day, energy from the heart of the atom was released by a machine, the nuclear reactor. Mankind had entered the Atomic Age.

The actual energy was hardly enough to light an electric bulb. But the tiny speck of matter from which it came was *three million times* more powerful than any fuel ever used. For five hundred thousand years, since the time that primitive man kindled the first spark of fire by rubbing two sticks together, every form of energy on the earth was created by the sun. Whether it came from wood, coal, oil gas, or the burning of food in our body cells, the energy was captured from the sun by a growing green plant.

In our factories and power houses, whether the wheels are turned mechanically or electrically, the sun is the primary source of the energy used. The coal with which we stoke our fires was once a plant that lived hundreds of millions of years ago; the trees we cut for firewood obtained their stored energy from the same source. Even the power of the windmill, and that of Niagara Falls is made possible by the sun's heat, for without it the air would not move, and the rivers would freeze.

On that fateful December afternoon, only a handful of men, and one woman, witnessed the tapping of a new source of energy, one that did not originate in the sun. The reactor which now lights the streets and homes of Northwest England, and furnishes the power for a plutonium factory, had its beginning in the atomic 'spark' produced in the squash tennis court building of the University of Chicago. That experiment with the first atomic pile proved that the atom could be made to do work.

THE ATOM'S first duty was to go to war. On July 16, 1945, at the precise moment of 5:30 A. M. Rocky Mountain Time, the first test bomb was exploded in the Almagordo Desert of New Mexico. The atomic flash, brighter than 'many suns,' followed a few seconds later by the mighty rolling thunder of the explosion, was dramatic proof of man's new mastery over matter. The blinding light, the deafening rumbling roar heard more than a hundred miles away, the strong surge of heat, and the mushroom-shaped cloud rising seven-and-a-half miles into the air — all these spectacularly proclaimed man's ability and determination to compete with the sun.

Both the explosion of an A-bomb and the production of energy by an atomic engine depend upon the same 'fuel.' There is a difference, however, like that between throwing a lighted match into a gas tank, and the slower, steady ignition of the gasoline-air mixture in the carburetor of an automobile. The first is triggered by the all-at-once speed of atomic particles called *neutrons*, while in the second these same particles are slowed down in order to control the energy release. Curiously enough, the controlled reaction had to be developed first, because the manufacture of atomic 'dynamite' required materials converted by the reactor.

The knowledge that made the bomb possible didn't grow out of the war, nor was atomic energy at any time a national secret. Step by step, the piling up of fact and theory had already been going on for some fifty years. Piece by piece, like the pattern of an intricate mosaic, the component parts of the atom had been discovered and its structure determined. Scientists throughout the world had been investigating the energy in the atom's core, or nucleus. As a matter of historical fact, Germany had a head start, in the attempt to make an atom-fired bomb. But as it turned out, the exclusion by the Nazis of any science (or scientists) that was not what they called 'Aryan' was one of the causes of their own destruction.

Several years before Pearl Harbor there were scientists, refugees from European Fascism and Nazism who were working both in England and the United States. These scientists alerted the Allied governments to the real threat of a German-made atomic weapon, and, with the physicists of their adopted countries, entered the race against time and a ruthless enemy.

WHAT FOLLOWS is the story of the men and women whose lifetime work as physicists and chemists carried man across the threshold of a new era. The man-in-the-street called them 'longhairs,' for they were supposed to be a little odd, isolated in their laboratories, lost in their brain-storms, careless about their dress, forgetful of their belongings, indifferent to the social amenities. Of course, it was understood that once in a while they might hatch an idea that would turn out to be useful.

Who were these people of the great fraternity of scientists — people from Poland, Scotland, New Zealand, Austria, Hungary, the Soviet Union, Italy, France, Denmark, Germany, Canada, England, the United States? What were they like as children and how did they fare in school? Did they have fun and personal hobbies? Did it all come easy to them? Were they rich or poor, were they ambitious, or did they give no thought to the morrow?

Our story tells about these people, their schooling, their family life, and their work. It begins with a girl who had to struggle against heartbreaking odds, and it ends with a New York City boy who seemingly had everything he could possibly desire. What moved these two, and the others in between, to choose the straight but difficult path of man's search for knowledge, and through it the conquest of nature for the ultimate good of all?

1. *Henri Antoine Becquerel.*

2. *How Becquerel Performed His Historic Experiment. A photograph was wrapped in black paper, then in aluminum foil. Uranyl salt crystals were placed on top. The result is shown in the illustration below.*

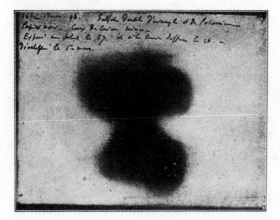

3. *Photographic plate, resulting from Becquerel's experiment, showing the first evidence of radioactivity that he sought. (The writing is Becquerel's.)*

MARIE AND PIERRE CURIE

(1867–1934)   (1859–1906)

A Strange Power in a New Element

IN A SMALL CORNER of a laboratory in the School of Physics, on the Rue Lhomond in Paris, a physicist was trying to choose an original subject for her thesis. Candidates for a doctor's degree usually discussed suitable topics with the professor under whose direction they would work. But it was different with Marie Curie. By 1897 she already had made her mark as an experienced scientist. Now in her thirtieth year, she had two university degrees, a fellowship in physics, and had just completed a book on her speciality, the magnetization of tempered steel. Her work had been interrupted hardly at all by the birth of her daughter Irene: when the baby was only two months old, Mme. Curie was back in the laboratory, working with her husband, Pierre. But what would she choose for a thesis?

One subject in particular attracted her. It had to do with an accidental but remarkable discovery made the previous year by the French scientist Henri Becquerel, while he was studying fluorescent substances (materials which glow softly after exposure to light). He in turn was fascinated by the work of Wilhelm Konrad Roentgen, who in 1895 had announced a new type of radiation which he called 'X' rays, the algebraic symbol for an unknown quantity. X-rays were both powerful and mysterious: they passed through opaque matter such as wood, glass, and even metal, fluorescent salts glowed under their impact, they darkened a photographic plate, and they even penetrated human flesh to produce a photographic record of the underlying bones.

While Becquerel was experimenting with his fluorescent substances (among them a yellow salt of the heavy metal uranium) to see if they would give off X-rays, he accidentally left a bit of this salt on a photographic plate in his darkroom. Some days later, on a hunch, he developed the plate. Something extraordinary had happened – a rough shadow of the pile of salt was silhouetted on the plate. The salt had taken a photograph of itself without X-rays, or any other rays, and in the dark! Becquerel placed more salt on other plates, carefully wrapped them in black paper and stored them in complete darkness for several months. When he opened them he knew that the uranium salt was giving off a radiation of its own which, like X-rays, etched a picture on a photographic plate, and 'ionized' the air molecules around itself; that is, it changed air from an insulator into a conductor. Another element – thorium – possessed this same power.

Some time later, Marie Curie was to name this strange phenomenon *radioactivity*. But where, the Curies asked themselves, did the energy come from? And what was the nature of this radiation? What a subject for a doctor's thesis! A virgin field to explore, for no one had yet begun to study uranium rays. There was only one item of bibliography for Marie to study – the paper read by Becquerel in 1896 before the Acadamy of Science in Paris.

'It was a leap into great adventure, into an unknown realm,' wrote her daughter Eve, years later, about Marie

Curie's choice of a dissertation. But to understand all this better, let's go back to Marie's girlhood days in Poland, the country where she was born.

MARIE, nicknamed Manya, remembered her childhood days as happy ones. Born on November 7, 1867, in the city of Warsaw, she was the youngest in a well-ordered family of good standing. There was also Zosia, the eldest, who told stories as no one else could; Bronya, who was to be Marie's life-long friend; and Hela, the most beautiful. And there was Joseph, the only boy, of whom the sisters were understandably proud.

Like any normal child Marie had her dolls, blocks, and toys. She kneaded mud cakes, climbed trees, dug in the garden, picked berries, paddled in a nearby stream, ran races, played hide-and-seek, giggled, chattered, laughed, sang, and cried when teased. As in any family, there were minor squabbles among the children, and occasional tricks played on her by an older sister, but more often they played together and helped one another. When Bronya became bored with learning the alphabet, she played 'teacher' to Marie, both arranging the cardboard letters in different orders. This game resulted in Marie's learning to read when she was only four years old.

Vladislav Sklodovski, her father, was a physics teacher, while Mme. Sklodovska* was principal of a school for the daughters of Warsaw's best families. The Sklodovskis lived at the school until shortly after Marie was born, when her father became professor and under-inspector at the high school. This meant moving into a new apartment provided for them, and also her mother's having to give up her directorship of the boarding school.

Among the cherished things Marie remembered was her father's workroom: the large desk where the older children

* In Poland, as in other Slavic countries, the female ending on the last name is different from the male.

did their homework, the barometer hanging on one wall, and on the other the glass case which held so many fascinating objects – small cases, compasses, calipers, flasks, tubes, and the shiny intricate instruments her father took to his classes on the days he taught science. Standing on tip-toe to gaze at these wonderful objects, four-year-old Marie was satisfied just to be told the name – physics apparatus—for the things she was to use so familiarly and lovingly later in life.

Marie also remembered her mother's beauty, grace, and gentleness as much as the deep, warm, special love she received as the baby of the family. Mme. Sklodovska also played the piano, sang ballads, taught, sewed her children's clothing, and even learned the cobbler's trade. Often Marie watched her cut leather, and with sticky string and shoemaker's awl sew uppers to soles, turning out shoes for the busy feet of her growing children.

But a quiet sadness also surrounded her mother, for she had tuberculosis. Only when the children had grown up did they realize the meaning of her dry cough, pale and transparent skin, and their nightly prayers, to 'restore our mother's health.'

Marie was hardly out of her early school years when one family misfortune after another darkened her days, all but wiping out the memories of her peaceful and carefree childhood. Her mother was taken seriously ill and, with Zosia as a companion, had to go to a sanatorium in Nice, a seashore resort in southern France. When she returned a year later from her 'cure,' still ravaged with the disease that was shortly to end her life, it seemed to Marie that her mother had suddenly grown very old. Then, in the fall of that same year, her father suffered official disgrace – his position as under-inspector was taken away from him.

From her own experience at school Marie knew what it meant to be a Pole and a 'Russian subject,' for Warsaw was in the part of Poland that was under the rule of Czar

Nicholas. The oppressed people owed allegiance to a tyran-
nical foreign sovereign, and were spied upon by his officials,
police, and even professors. Were the teachers carrying out
their orders to wipe out all 'Polish-isms' among the rebel-
lious and patriotic people? Were they really teaching their
pupils the Russian language? Marie understood what must
have happened to her father: the inspector's visit had not
gone off as smoothly as one she remembered in her own
classroom.

One morning during a lesson in Polish history the teacher,
in her patriotic fervor, was addressing the twenty-five uniformed pupils in the Polish language. Two long and two
short rings of a bell gave the familiar signal that the inspector was about to enter. What a transformation in the classroom! Four little pupils carried off the Polish books in their
aprons. Out of the desks came scissors, spools of thread,
thimbles, and squares of cloth with unravelled edges. In
front of the teacher appeared a textbook printed in the
Greek alphabet of the Russian language. When the director
opened the door for the inspector, everything was in order.
The children were bent over their sewing, while the teacher
read aloud from a book of fairy tales. There were no books
or papers to betray them as the inspector opened the lid of
each desk.

Next he asked the teacher to call on one of the pupils to
recite. Every child, frightened, silently prayed that she
would not be the one, Marie more than any one else. But
she knew she could not escape. She was two years ahead of
her classmates, first in history, arithmetic, literature, German and French, and she spoke Russian perfectly.

'Recite your prayer,' ordered the inspector.

Without faltering, Marie repeated the words of 'Our
Father,' the Catholic prayer, the prayer of her faith, but in
the foreign language, a requirement that emphasized the
humiliation of her people.

'Name in proper order the Czars who have reigned over our Holy Russia since Catherine II.'

Marie answered this correctly, as well as questions about the names and titles of the imperial family, the order of the dignitaries in the Czar's palace, and the title of the inspector.

The final thrust was:

'Who rules over us?'

'His Majesty Alexander II, Czar of All the Russias.' The answer was painful, but the frightened child, even at her tender age, was already disciplined in the ways of quiet rebellion.

The ordeal was over and the spying interrogator departed. Released from her strain, Marie burst into tears as the teacher kissed her on the forehead.

But things didn't always go so successfully. On a similar visit, the superior in her father's school did not find everything in order, and he was punished.

As a result of her father's demotion, the Sklodovskis lost their apartment in the school and had to move several times, always to poorer quarters. To make ends meet, the Professor boarded young boys from the school – first only two or three, then as many as ten. The well-ordered, peaceful family life vanished, and things went from bad to worse. In a desperate effort to provide for his family and pay for his wife's treatment, Marie's father invested and lost his life savings in a venture proposed by an unscrupulous relative. For many years M. Sklodovski was to torment himself for having thus deprived his daughters of the dowries for which the money had been saved.

In the winter of 1876, the two older sisters caught typhus from one of the boarders. For weeks Bronya and Zosia shook with fever, until finally Zosia was taken from them. Two years later, sick and grieving, the mother died. For Marie, aged nine, the deaths of two of her most beloved were cruel blows. Everything gay and cheerful seemed to have departed

along with the tenderness of her mother and the companionship of her older sister. Her father, deeply saddened by his
wife's death, did all he could to care for the children with
the small salary and the little free time he had.

When Marie was fourteen years old, Joseph, who had
graduated from high school with a gold medal award, was
studying at the Faculty of Medicine in the University of
Warsaw (which did not admit women). Bronya, now a young
lady, also with honors and a gold medal from the government Gymnasium (high school), had taken over the manage-
ment of the household. Hela, still in the blue uniform of a
school girl, attended the private Sikorska school, and Marie
herself was one of the most brilliant pupils in the Gymnasium. The high school, run by the government, was
entirely Russian. Though the professors, hostile to the
Polish nation, treated the pupils as enemies, it was necessary
to attend a government school to obtain a diploma, since
the private schools could not grant one.

The animosity of teachers and superintendents only in-
tensified the hidden hatred which united the students
against their oppressors. Inside the classroom Polish,
Russian, Jewish, and German boys and girls rubbed
shoulders, helped each other in their work, and in fun and
play forgot the national differences. But once outside the
school walls they walked off in tight little groups, made
friends only with 'their own,' and would have thought it a
betrayal to invite an 'outsider' to their parties. No opportunity was missed to express their deep-seated rancor against
the enemy camp, even at considerable risk.

One day, for instance, Marie and Kazia, her dearest girlhood friend, while rolling hoops in the square near the
Palace of Saxony, passed the monument with the inscription
– in Russian letters – 'To the Poles faithful to their Sovereign.' For all patriots this was a disgusting object, the Czar's
tribute to those who had betrayed their countrymen. Absorbed in their play, the two girls had failed to observe the

custom of spitting as they passed the monument. Suddenly remembering, they turned back and solemnly carried out their duty.

These outbursts of rebellion did not, however, mar the fun and love of life that are part of the lives of all young people. There were parties, carnivals, and dances (Marie once wore out a pair of dancing shoes in a single night).

In June of 1883, Marie, like her brother and sister, completed her high school studies with a gold medal and other honors. She was not yet sixteen, and her father thought she was too young to choose a vocation. Besides, she had worked very hard, and he insisted that she spend a year in the country with relatives. This was perhaps the only year in her life when Marie was away from serious study and able to fully indulge her life-long passion for the countryside.

To her friend Kazie she wrote:

> I may say that aside from an hour's French lesson with a little boy I don't do a thing, positively not a thing. . . . We go out in a band to walk in the woods, we roll hoops, we play battledore and shuttlecock (at which I am very bad!).
>
> We swing a lot, we bathe, we go fishing with torches for shrimps. . . . Every Sunday the horses are harnessed for the trip in to Mass. . . .

THE CAREFREE holiday over, Marie returned to Warsaw to find the family in smaller and poorer quarters, but for that very reason leading a more peaceful and satisfying home life, for M. Sklodovski had decided not to take in any boarders. When not teaching he was now able to study the latest publications in physics and chemistry; he translated foreign authors into Polish, and even composed poetry. On Saturday evenings the four children gathered around to hear him recite poetry, read travel stories, and translate works from English into their native tongue. His enduring thirst for knowledge was an inspiration to all his children, but most of all to Marie, who at this time of her life believed that her father knew everything.

When they became old enough to earn a living, it was natural for them to turn first to tutoring. And so Marie began to answer newspaper advertisements requesting private lessons. Tutoring was neither rewarding nor easy to get (there were many others who wanted the work). Walking across the city in all kinds of weather, waiting for indifferent or lazy pupils, the humiliation of reminding parents that the meager payment was due — all this Marie accepted as necessary, but secretly she dreamed of a different future.

Barred from a higher education because of their sex, young girls like Marie, with a passion for learning, joined small groups called Floating Universities. They met secretly in private homes, taught one another, and passed on their knowledge to working women and poor housewives, by reading aloud to them in the Polish language. Reminiscing about this period of her life, Marie wrote:

> I persist in believing that the ideas that then guided us are the only ones which can lead to true social progress. We cannot hope to build a better world without improving the individual. Toward this end, each of us must work toward his own highest development, accepting at the same time his share of responsibility in the general life of humanity. . . .

At the age of seventeen, Marie gave up tutoring for the position of governess with a family living in the country. She hated to leave her aged, tired father and the warmth of life at home, and at first was overcome with homesickness. But she soon found compensations in her work. The younger children of her employer — a wealthy agriculturist — liked her immediately, and the eldest daughter, her own age, became a bosom companion. She enjoyed walks in the country, gay excursions with the family, and sleigh riding and ice-skating in the winter. She also helped bring in the beet crop and care for the horses, which she rode often.

After her charges had gone to bed, she would read literature and study sociology and the physical sciences. She organized classes for the village children, furnished them and their parents with books borrowed from the beet-sugar factory, and so earned their love and gratitude. Even this was dangerous, because it was forbidden by the government, and was punishable by imprisonment or deportation to Siberia.

Still Marie was determined to go to a university and render greater service to her beloved country. But how was she to manage it without means? An idea hatched in her young and active mind, one that took into account both her own and Bronya's consuming ambition. At first her sister wouldn't hear of it, but the logic of the idea, together with her deep desire for study, finally won Bronya over.

Marie's plan was simple: she was to continue as governess, and save every penny until she had enough to send her sister to Paris to study medicine. When Bronya's studies were completed (with Marie's continuing help), she in turn would work and save enough to bring Marie to Paris.

Three long years of work followed, with all her savings going to Bronya. Letters to Kazya and Joseph tell of her sadness, discouragement, and the kind of poverty that delays letter writing until a stamp can be bought. '. . . now that I have lost hope of ever becoming anybody, all my ambition has been transferred to Bronya and you,' she wrote to her brother. Then in 1889 her employers decided they no longer needed a governess. Marie went back to Warsaw and found a position with another wealthy family for whom she worked for two years.

Letters from Paris were heartening. Bronya was doing well in her studies and was working besides. She was in love. The young man, Casimir Dluski, also a medical student and a Pole, was unable to return to Russian Poland because of the threat of deportation to Siberia. They were to marry as soon as they received their medical degrees, and they planned to live in Paris.

By this time Marie's father had retired on a small pension, but in order to help his daughters financially, he accepted the directorship of a Warsaw reform school. The work was distasteful, but the salary enabled M. Sklodovski to give a monthly allowance to Bronya. In a short while she wrote Marie not to send any more money. At the same time, she asked her father to keep for her younger sister the money he had been sending her.

Meanwhile Marie used her evenings and Sundays to learn mathematics and physics. And while 'studying chemistry out of a book', she occasionally worked in a small laboratory – directed by a cousin – conducting experiments in the physical sciences. Often she despaired at the slowness of self-teaching but she was impelled to go on and at last the letter came from Bronya: 'And now you, my little Manya, you must make something of your life some time. If you can get together a few hundred rubles this year you can come to Paris next year and live with us, where you will find board and lodging.'

Fifteen months later, in the fall of 1891, Marie counted up her savings. There was enough to cover her passport, her railway ticket (fourth-class through Germany) and freight for her trunk (with mattress, bed-clothes, and everything that would make buying anything in Paris unnecessary). For the three-day journey she took food and drink, a folding chair for the German carriage, a quilt, and a bag of caramels. As Marie parted from her father, she promised tearfully that she would be back in two or at the most three years, to settle down as a teacher in her native town. But as her daughter later wrote: 'She was far, very far from thinking that when she entered this train she had at last chosen between obscurity and a blazing light, between the pettiness of equal days and an immense life.'

PARIS AT LAST! A girlhood dream come true, and for one coming from Czarist Poland a wondrous liberation as well. Freedom for the first time to speak one's own language, to see the world's great literary works openly displayed on the bookstalls, and to have the right to buy them. For little Marie Sklodovska this was truly a miracle. Even more of a miracle was her actual registration in the Faculty of Sciences of a real University, and what a University – the Sorbonne, 'most celebrated and excellent of schools'! Here she would listen to lectures by famed professors in courses of her own choice, work in a real laboratory, receive guidance in carrying out experiments, with apparatus she would be taught to use. A fairy tale could be no more unbelievable.

She always sat in a front seat, her whole being intent on learning, and never noticed the curious eyes of her classmates, staring at the foreign student in the threadbare black woolen dress, the ash-blond hair brushed back from her beautifully arched forehead, the pale face illuminated with deep gray eyes. She was blind to all but the wonders of the laws governing the universe, the harmonious principles that explain the world and its mysteries, and she was learning things infinitely more exciting and absorbing than anything she had ever read in fairy tales or novels. For science explained real things as they were, and led to ever new and unexplored paths.

But first she discovered that her scientific preparation – acquired solely through self-study, correspondence with her father, and hit-or-miss attempts at experimentation in the small Warsaw laboratory – had left many gaps in the knowledge she needed for the university courses. Then she found that her French was not as perfect as she had thought: much of what was said in the classroom escaped her. In addition to the regular work, these deficiences had to be made up.

For the first few months Marie lived with the Dluskis. Bronya and Casimir, both physicians, were now living in a

small flat in the Rue d'Allemagne, in a part of Paris inhabited by many of their Polish compatriots. Their home
served also as their office. Marie enjoyed the hospitality and
companionship of her older sister and her charming, solici-
tous brother-in-law, but there were drawbacks. The doctors
worked hard and needed their evenings for relaxation.
Guests from the Polish colony visited them, or they attended
concerts, theatres, and such other cultural entertainment as
they could afford, and Marie had to go along. There were
other distractions — visits from patients, night calls for
Bronya — and besides the flat was an hour's ride from the
University, and required a double fare. Because she be-
grudged every minute spent from her studies, Marie finally
decided to exchange her cheerful home for the isolation of
a room near the university.

By leaving the Dluskis she gave up her free board and
lodging, and this sorely strained the monthly budget of forty
rubles her savings permitted (about 100 francs or 20 dollars).
Other foreign students stretched their meager allowances by
sharing room and board with two or three others, but Marie
prized her solitude, and would not surrender a minute for
unnecessary housekeeping.

For three years she lived in an attic room furnished with
an iron bed, the mattress she had brought from home, a
kitchen table and chair, washbasin, kerosene lamp, alcohol
burner for cooking, and a small coal stove. She ate little more
than bread, fruit, an egg, and a cup of chocolate, rarely going
into a butcher shop, for meat was an undreamed luxury.
Coal, when not forgotten or excluded by her budget, had
to be carried up six flights to the cold, austere room. At
times it was so cold that the water in the basin froze during
the night, while Marie tried to keep warm by piling her
clothes on the blanket. An occasional visitor enjoyed the
hospitality of tea made on the alcohol burner, and a seat on
the trunk, which doubled as wardrobe and chest of drawers.
Even kerosene was kept down to the barest minimum.

Whenever possible Marie ran off to the library as soon as it became too dark to read by twilight.

Bronya and Casimir, though worried about her pinched and worn appearance, never suspected the extent of the young girl's privation and fatigue, until one day she fainted in the classroom. A student brought her home and then rushed to notify her family, but when Dr. Dluski arrived, Marie was back at her studies. After examining not only the patient, but also the food cupboard – empty of anything but a package of tea – he realized that she had fainted from starvation. His questions revealed that she had eaten only a few radishes and cherries since the night before. It needed only some wholesome food during a week at the Dluskis to bring the color back to her cheeks, and before she left they made her promise to take care of herself in the future.

Back in her cherished solitude, Marie returned to her studies and chosen way of life. In April of 1893, she wrote to her father: 'The nearer the examinations come, the more I am afraid of not being ready.' But when July arrived, and the students gathered to hear the results, Marie Sklodovska's name was the first to be called! She was graduated with the highest honors as 'licencée ès Sciences Physiques,' and the following year, aided by the Alexandrovitch Scholarship of 600 rubles, with the second highest honors, as 'licencée ès Sciences Mathematiques,' the equivalents of master's degrees in physics and mathematics. (To the amazement of the secretary of the Alexandrovitch Foundation, she later returned the money as payment of a debt of honor, and as a means for helping another young student). The degrees in her two major fields of life-long interest marked the end of what Dr. Dluski called 'the heroic period of my sister-in-law's life,' the wonderful solitary years devoted exclusively to study. What now?

In her last year at the Sorbonne, she wrote to her brother: 'I shall write soon to Joseph Boguski and ask him for information about his laboratory. My future occupation depends on this.' But the course of her life, which up to now she had charted by the force of her determination, was to take an unexpected turn. In her passion for science, Marie seemed to have renounced everything else. There was little or no time in her life for leisure and social contacts. Except for her great attachment to family and fatherland, she lived in her own private universe.

But during her last year in Paris, a Polish professor, lecturing and attending sessions of the Physics Society, inquired after Marie, whom he had known when she was a governess. Always glad to see one of her countrymen, Marie accepted an invitation to his home, perhaps even more eagerly because she had a problem in physics to solve. She had been assigned by the Society for the Encouragement of National Industry to study the magnetic properties of various steels, and needed analytical apparatus not available in her laboratory. Professor Kovalski had an idea: he would introduce her to a well-known scientist of the School of Physics and Chemistry in the Rue Lhomond. Thus Marie met Pierre Curie, at the home of Professor Kovalski.

Let Marie describe him for us: '. . . a tall young man with auburn hair and large, limpid eyes. . . . I noticed the grave and gentle expression of his face, as well as a certain abandon in his reflections.' The second son of a physician, he had not gone to school because his father, Dr. Eugène Curie, had recognized in him an extraordinary student who would only be held back by the average scholastic pace. At first the doctor himself did the teaching, then later engaged a private tutor. The result was that Pierre received a bachelor's degree at sixteen, a master's degree in physics at eighteen, and for several years worked with his brother Jacques in the physics laboratory at the Sorbonne.

When Marie met Pierre, he was thirty-five years old, and already chief of the laboratory at the School of Physics and Chemistry of the City of Paris. He and his brother had discovered the fact that an electric charge appears on certain crystals if a weight is placed on them. Thus, they invented a new apparatus—the *piezoelectric quartz* which measured small amounts of electricity with great accuracy. Going on to research into the physical properties of crystals, he formulated the principle of *symmetry* in crystalline structures. By now his work was receiving international recognition. The celebrated English scientist, Lord Kelvin, wrote to him: '. . . [regarding] the magnificent experimental discovery of piezoelectric quartz, made by you and your brother, I have written a note for the *Philosophical Magazine,* making it clear that your work preceded mine.'

Pierre was as completely devoted to science as Marie was to her studies, and he had given no thought to personal attachments. Many years before he met Marie, he wrote in his diary: '. . . Woman loves life for the living of it far more than we do: women of genius are rare.' But he must have recognized in Marie one of those rare women, for during the rest of that year they saw each other at Physics Society meetings, in the laboratory where she worked, and in her barren garret room. At last Pierre told her how much he wanted her to visit his parents, with whom he lived in a modest home in Sceaux, a suburb of Paris.

The more they saw of each other, the greater grew their friendship and admiration for each other. It was Marie who stimulated Pierre to complete his brilliant doctor's thesis on magnetism, and it was he who helped Marie prepare for her examinations. When she left Paris for the summer, Pierre was ready to follow her to Poland, to work with her, to give French lessons, if necessary – a sacrifice Marie told him she had no right to permit.

In the fall of 1894, Marie returned and re-entered the Sorbonne to begin experimental research for her doctor's thesis, and of course she again saw Pierre. Their work continued to draw them closer, until, as she wrote years later: 'We were both convinced that neither of us could find a better life companion.'

4. *The Sklodowska children: Zosia, Hela, Maria, Joseph, and Bronia.*

5. *The Curie family: Pierre, his brother Jacques, and their mother and father.*

On July 26, 1895, Mlle. Marie Sklodovska became Mme. Pierre Curie. Hela and M. Sklodovska came to Paris to attend the simple wedding. There was no white dress, no gold ring, no wedding breakfast. The bride wore a plain blue woolen suit that was 'practical and dark' (and could be worn later in the laboratory). The honeymoon was to be a trip on bicycles bought with money they had received as a wedding gift.

Both loved the simple pleasures of roaming the countryside, so they made no elaborate plans. They strapped their luggage to the bicycles and rode from place to place, staying overnight in village inns, sometimes leaving their bicycles and following some trail into the woods, taking only a compass, fruit, and cheese. They were completely happy in their solitude, loving the same things, planning the dedication of their lives to science. With poetic insight Eve Curie writes of those happy days: 'Two minds of genius learned to think together.'

The young couple settled in a three-room apartment at 24 Rue de la Glacière, near the Physics School, where Marie obtained authorization to work with her husband. In addition to doing research on the magnetic properties of steel, Marie studied for a teaching certificate. At the end of one year Marie passed first in the examination, and began teaching in a girl's school, while Pierre went on with his research on the physics of crystals.

Their little flat faced a large garden, but it was almost bare of furniture and devoid of the simplest comforts. Pierre made only 500 francs a month, about the same as a factory worker, but for this modest couple, one of whom was an expert in economy, the salary was adequate. Still, life was hard for Marie. She put in a full day's work at the laboratory, kept the apartment, and did all of the marketing, cleaning, and cooking. Of necessity she had to learn to cook – something she had never bothered with before. Diligently she read cook books, less from interest than duty, noting in the margin the reason for the failure of a recipe, and how next time to concoct a culinary success. With a scientist's precision she would adjust the flame in the morning so that the meat would 'roast itself,' and be done but unburned when they returned in the evening.

In 1896, after Marie had won the competitive fellowship in Secondary Education, they took time off to bicycle to Auvergne and Cevennes, and made several trips to the seashore. Marie particularly enjoyed swimming, and excelled in it. Then the following year, on September 12, 1897, their first daughter, Irène, was born. That same year Marie completed and published her work on the magnetic properties of steel.

A few weeks after Irène's birth, Pierre's mother died. Pierre and Marie left their flat and rented a small house and garden at the edge of the city where Dr. Eugène came to live with them. Every day, before leaving for the laboratory, Marie attended to the baby, and returned in time for her supper feeding and bedtime care. Dr. Curie helped with the household duties, but life was so full that little time was left for social life and friends. Even Bronya and Casimir were gone: they had left for Poland to set up a sanatorium.

LATE in the fall Marie embarked upon her life work. She had obtained the use of a glassed-in studio on the ground floor of the school. It was cold and damp, cluttered with unused equipment and lumber, and she had to make do with crude equipment, except for the sensitive electrometer, which took no more kindly to the changing humidity and temperature of the bleak little hole than did its user. But with this instrument, invented by Pierre and Jacques Curie, Marie first tested the power of uranium rays to ionize air, making it an electrical conductor.

After several weeks of experimentation, she was able to report amazing results: the intensity of radiation was proportional to the quantity of uranium used, *regardless of its chemical combination with other elements.* Moreover, the radiation was not affected by either light or temperature changes. The rays were like nothing else known: *nothing affected them!* It was not long before Marie knew that she was dealing with an *atomic* property, a property of the element uranium, regardless of the salt in which it was combined. Now was this true *only* of uranium, or were there other elements with this power of radiation?

She lost no time in trying other chemicals, both pure and in compounds, and her next startling discovery was that *thorium* compounds emitted rays like those of uranium. It had to be that elements other than uranium could give off a 'radiance.' Marie proposed that this power be called *radioactivity,* and one after another she gave the electrometer test to every chemical, every salt and oxide, that she and Pierre could pick up in the laboratory. *Only* those containing uranium or thorium were radioactive. All others were 'inactive.'

Then one day she found an 'error'; one mineral was much more radioactive than could be accounted for by the uranium and thorium in it. Where could it come from? Marie repeated the measurement dozens of times, until she was convinced there was no mistake. Did this mineral contain something new? After all, they had already examined every known element! Could she have come upon a *new* element? It was a bold thought, but the idea persisted, and nothing could persuade the stubborn scientist to set it aside.

'You know, Bronya,' she told her sister, 'the radiation that I couldn't explain comes from a new chemical element. The element is there and I've got to find it. We are sure! The physicists we have spoken to believe we have made an error. . . . But I am convinced that I am not mistaken.'

The next spring Marie Sklodovska Curie, in a communication to the Academy of Sciences that was published in its proceedings, proposed that *pitchblende ore* probably contained a new element with powerful radioactivity. Just what it was still had to be verified by experiment; its existence had to be proved. Pierre shared her conviction, so much so that he set aside his study of crystals and joined his wife in the immense task of extracting and identifying the illusive element. From that very moment, and for the next eight years, the Curies were to work so closely together in achieving one of the greatest discoveries of all time, that their individual contributions are impossible to distinguish. From that moment on, their notes always read, '*We* observed,' '*We* found.'

THE CRUDE ore of pitchblende proved to be four times as active as the pure oxide of uranium extracted from it. The Curies reasoned that since the composition of this ore had been known for a long time, the 'new element' must be present in very small amounts. How else could it have escaped the notice of chemists who had analyzed it repeatedly? But just how much was there? One per cent was a small amount, yet how much more remarkable was their discovery that this powerful radioactive element was only *one-millionth* part of pitchblende ore!

Then began the painstaking months-long chemical analysis of pitchblende. One fraction after another was eliminated, until only two were left. By July, 1898, they were ready to announce their discovery of one of the two. Giving in to Pierre's insistence that she select its name, Marie christened it *polonium,* after Poland, the country of her birth. She wondered whether its discovery would be announced in Russia and Austria – the oppressors of her fatherland.

The Proceedings of the Academy for July, 1898, carried this item:

> We believe the substance we have extracted from pitch-blende contains a metal not yet observed, related to bismuth by its analytical properties. If the existence of this new metal is confirmed we propose to call it *polonium,* from the name of the original country of one of us.

After that they spoke of their new metals as polonium and 'the other,' but not for long. Before the end of that year the Curies announced their discovery of the chemical twin – *radium*. 'The new radioactive substance certainly contains a very strong proportion of barium; in spite of that its radio-activity is considerable. The radioactivity of radium there-fore must be enormous.'

But did this 'enormous' potential radioactivity mean that they had really discovered a new element? Was it a new *thing* or only a phantom in the imagination of the two scientists? It was like discovering a track, a footprint, a shadow, but not the substance itself. Besides, argued the physicists, it upset so many accepted ideas! Where can radi-ation energy come from, all by itself, spontaneously, without a force to release it? The chemists posed an even more important problem. They said a substance must have weight, atomic weight.* Could radium be weighed on a scale? What did it look like and feel like, and could it be combined with anything? One must be able to see it, meas-ure it, 'weigh' it. Said the chemists: 'We will believe radium exists if you show it to us.' The job now was to *produce* radium, for everyone to see, a job that took four solid years of work. Since radium was but a tiny speck in pitchblende, it would take enormous quantities of the ore to yield a per-ceptible amount of its radioactive fraction. Tons would be needed, pitchblende was an expensive ore, and there were very few places where it could be obtained. The nearest was the St. Joachimsthal mine in Bohemia, where pitchblende was extracted from the earth for its uranium salts, which were separated out for use in glass-making and ceramics. It was the unwanted residue, the Curies believed, that con-tained their hidden element. Perhaps the mine owners would be glad to get rid of it? They would, and the scientists

* A number expressing how much heavier an atom of any substance is compared with hydrogen, the lightest, whose atomic weight is 1. An atom of oxygen is 16 times heavier, therefore its atomic weight is said to be 16.

could have it for the cost of transporting it to France. It took all of their savings, but Pierre and Marie paid for the shipment to Paris of tons and tons of pitchblende residue.

Now where could they work over this mass of material? To carry on the chemical separation, they needed lots of room and huge cauldrons. Right outside Marie's little workroom there was an old wooden shed. Yes, they could have it, said the school authorities. Of course the roof leaked, and there was no floor, and the only heat came from an old iron stove with a rusty pipe. But what did the scientists care? They had a place to receive the first ton of ore the mine director was willing to give to 'the foolish two people.'

From 1898 to 1902 the Curies worked ceaselessly, trying to separate radium from pitchblende. It was killing work: pouring off the liquids, stirring for hours the boiling matter in the smelting basin, keeping the fire going. Days wore into weeks, weeks into months, but still they had no pure radium.

Yet with each stage of purification – *fractional crystallization* – the product became more concentrated, and according to their measurements, more radioactive. With infinite patience, kilogram by kilogram, they treated the tons of pitchblende received from St. Joachimsthal. As the work continued, their difficulties increased; with each new refinement it became more and more important to have a spotlessly clean laboratory, uncontaminated with coal dust and wind-blown dirt. The measuring instrument had to be kept clean and protected from temperature and moisture changes.

Because of the miserable conditions under which they were forced to work there were times when Pierre was ready to abandon the project until they could secure a decent laboratory. But Marie pushed on and on, day after day, even night after night, without regard for fatigue or discomfort.

By 1902, they had succeeded in preparing only one-tenth of a gram of pure radium (about one three-hundreth of an ounce). But it was enough to determine its atomic weight, and they announced to the world a new substance, with an atomic weight of 225. They had proved the existence of radium!

Radium didn't have the beautiful color its discoverers had dreamed of. But in the darkness of the night its emanating rays made the little glass bottles glow with the brilliance of myriads of glowworms. It was spontaneously luminous — giving off penetrating rays as its atoms were disintegrating, constantly changing.

The unbelieving chemists 'could only bow before the facts, before the superhuman obstinacy of a woman,' writes Eve Curie. The physicists, too, were convinced.

THEIR GREAT discovery didn't make the next four years any easier. Pierre was still earning only 500 francs a month, directing students' experiments at the School of Physics. He needed more money, more time for research, a laboratory, electrical installations, technical equipment, room for an assistant or two, and a little heat in winter. Even these modest needs were not met; despite world recognition, the Curies had to struggle against governmental indifference in making appropriations for research, against petty jealousies and competitions in gaining a better post, and in Pierre's taking his rightful place as a member of the Academy. Pierre lost out against a much less-known candidate in the first election, and was elected by only a slim margin the second time he was nominated.

Not until 1904 was Pierre made a professor at the Sorbonne. This gave him a little more money and time, but he was never to realize his ambition of working in a new laboratory. Rather than spend their time persuading officials in government bureaus, they preferred to work under the continuing severely trying circumstances.

Marie supplemented the family income by teaching physics students in the Normal School at Sèvres. Several times a week she traveled by slow tram to the school, carrying home a briefcase of homework to correct. So much time taken away from the work they were dedicated to! Worst of all, Pierre was not well. Subject to violent attacks of pain from rheumatism, he moaned through many sleepless nights that left him weak for days afterward.

It was June 25, 1903, at the Sorbonne. Madame Sklodovska Curie was to present her dissertation for approval by the examiners – *Researches on Radioactive Substances.* Never had a more important work been submitted as a doctor's thesis. But from the traditionally austere and simple ceremony, one could not have distinguished between this discovery by a genius and the work of an ordinary conscientious student. The young candidate quietly answered the questions of the three examiners and when it was over, the President intoned the formal routine pronouncement: 'The University of Paris accords you the title of doctor of physical science, with the mention of *très honorable.*'

In addition to the effect of the theory of radioactive transformation of matter on the established idea that atoms are forever the same – sodium is always sodium, gold is always gold – the discovery by the Curies was to have immediate practical results for mankind. Here was radium, two million times more radioactive than uranium, giving off penetrating rays which only a thick plate of lead could stop. These were the gamma rays. It also gave off two other kinds of radiation: in an electric and magnetic field one fraction – the *beta* particles – were deflected (bent) to one side, as if they carried a negative charge, and the *alpha* particles, 7000 times as heavy as the betas, were deflected to the opposite side. Moving much more slowly than either beta or gamma rays (about 10,000 miles per second) the alpha particles were *ions,* charged particles of the gas *helium.*

But it was the gamma rays that captured the imagination of the scientists at this time. Shooting off spontaneously

6. *The Curies' "laboratory" on rue Lhomond, Paris.*

7. *Marie and Pierre Curie with their bicycles at Sceaux.*

from radium, these rays made an impression on photographic plates through black paper. This new substance made an electrical conductor of air; it was luminous; it corroded the paper or cotton in which it was wrapped; it produced a 'ghost' (a gaseous substance called the 'emanation'); spontaneously it gave off an enormous quantity of heat; and finally it destroyed itself!

In 1900, two Germans announced that radium had strange effects on living tissue. Following this up, Pierre Curie exposed his arms to radiations, and reported with joy that the skin became red as if from a burn. 'I may add that Mme. Curie, in carrying a few centigrams of very active matter in a little sealed tube, received analogous burns, even though the little tube was enclosed in a thin metallic box,' he reported. Henri Becquerel was also burned while carrying a glass tube of radium in his coat pocket. 'I love this radium, but I've got a grudge against it,' he told the Curies.

All this, strangely enough, proved that radium was immediately useful. It destroyed tissue. Why not train its deadly rays on cancer, which it would heal by destroying the rapidly growing sick cells? The Academy of Sciences provided 20,000 francs for the Curies, and in 1904, an enterprising French industrialist, Armet de Lisle, set up a factory where Pierre, Marie, and a few assistants worked on the separation of radium, to be furnished to doctors for the treatment of cancerous tumors.

(Marie was never to part with the first gram of radium they extracted. She donated it to the Laboratory, where it was guarded as the shining symbol of a great scientific contribution. When the Germans threatened to occupy Paris in World War I, Marie carried the precious radium, in a fifty-pound lead case, to a remote town where she deposited it in a bank vault to keep it safe from the hands of the invader.)

Succeeding grams, selling at about $150,000 a piece — the most expensive substance in the world — were to be used to save people's lives. Pierre and Marie Curie had by that time made a selfless and momentous decision, the technique they had invented (still used in the preparation of radium) was to be the property of mankind – they would not patent it. They published their results in full, and answered all questions that poured in from every part of the world. 'If our discovery has a commercial future, that is an accident by which we must not profit. And radium is going to be of use in treating disease. . . .'

In 1903, honors began to shower upon the two shy, modest physicists. From the Royal Society of London came its highest award, the Davy medal. Soon afterwards, the Academy of Science of Stockholm announced that the year's Nobel Prize for physics would go half to Becquerel, and half to the Curies for their discovery of radioactivity. But Marie and Pierre, overworked and ill, were not present at the ceremony: the diplomas and medals were sent to them through the French Minister.

These and hundreds of other honors that came to them jointly, and to Marie after her husband's tragic death, were more disturbing than gratifying. The many expressions of appreciation from a grateful world for their gift to mankind only upset the peace and quiet of this simple pair, who had given their lives to science, and had no taste for fame.

When the 70,000 francs of the Nobel Prize were deposited in the bank, Pierre gave up his position at the School of Physics, where he was replaced by his celebrated pupil, Paul Langevin. Twenty thousand went to the Dluskis for their sanatorium. Money and presents were given to scientific societies, childhood friends of Marie's, students, laboratory assistants. They bought a few small luxuries for their home, but never gave a thought, on this proud occasion, to getting even a new hat for Marie. The first woman ever to be awarded the Nobel Prize continued to teach at the Sèvres school for girls.

THEN CAME the great tragedy in Marie's life. On a rainy morning in April, 1906, Pierre was killed instantly, his head crushed by a wagon wheel, as he tripped on the wet pavement trying to avoid the rearing horse. Marie lost her loving husband, her inseparable partner in their life work, and the world lost a great man.

Saddened by her deep grief, the years ahead were to be infinitely harder for her to bear. Now she must shoulder alone the responsibility of caring for two young daughters (Eve was born in 1904), and the aging Dr. Curie, earning her livelihood, continuing the work on radium, and filling her husband's place as a professor. Marie made a super-human effort to carry on, always remembering Pierre's words when they talked about the possibility of what was now a bitter reality: 'Whatever happens, even if one has to go on like a body without a soul, one must work just the same.'

One task she undertook with dedication and love: the building of the laboratory Pierre had dreamed of where young men and women could develop the new science of radioactivity. Also she was to teach at the Sorbonne, where for the first time a woman would hold a professorship

Marie was thirty-eight when Pierre died. Almost half of her adult life was still ahead of her. The fragile, tired, and lonely little woman threw herself into her work with a passion, courage, and energy seldom found even in a robust giant. The later achievements of her richly fruitful life hardly seem possible of accomplishment by one person.

In 1908 she collected and put in order the *Works of Pierre Curie,* and in 1910 published her own *Treatise on Radioactivity.* A year later she made a second determination of the atomic weight of radium, discovered a method of measuring radium by its emanation, and prepared the first international standard of radium with which all samples in the world are compared. She taught hundreds of students and directed their research while personally supervising the famous Paris Institute of Radium. During World War I she organized the army medical service, set up the first X-ray-equipped stations on the battlefront, and founded the course for technicians in X-ray techniques.

During these years she attended dozens of scientific congresses, lectures and university ceremonies, visited foreign laboratories, became vice-president of the International Committee on Intellectual Cooperation (of the League of Nations), made two trips to America, on each occasion receiving a gram of radium (one for the Institute of Radium of Warsaw), and trained workers of many nationalities in her laboratory.

In 1911, she again received the Nobel Prize, this time in chemistry, the first person to receive the honor twice. In all the world's capitals she was welcomed and fêted, acclaimed as a deliverer by the people of every nation.

Only her adopted country, which she served so nobly both in peace and in war, was late in giving her recognition. Because she was a woman, she was refused admission to the Academy of Sciences, and denied the only honor she ever craved — a soldier's decoration for her war service. She suffered sniping campaigns set going by envious colleagues, and was harassed and humiliated by the newspapers, who called her Jewess, Catholic, Russian, German, Pole, or just 'the foreign woman.' Government officials slighted her when she solicited funds for the Radium Institute.

Poor and self-negating to the end, ill and almost blind, oblivious to personal comforts, scornful of precautions which she imposed upon her pupils in the handling of radioactive materials, indifferent to fashion or adornment, the once beautiful woman always dressed in a simple black dress and worked twelve to fifteen hours a day — until the miraculous metal she had discovered destroyed her blood-forming tissue, causing her death. She died in July, 1934, from leukemia (cancer of the bone marrow). and radium was her killer.

Radium, which caused Marie Curie's death, was to bring health and longer life to many sick people. For this alone her discovery would have made her one of the immortals. But her contribution to atomic energy was perhaps even more important. For the first time it was shown that the atom was not indivisible; it gave off particles; atoms could change, and their disintegration yielded enormous amounts of energy.

JOSEPH JOHN THOMSON

(1856–1940)

Discovery of the Electron

OUR STORY NOW TAKES US back to about the time when
Marie Curie was born. The place: Cambridge, England,
where a laboratory for research in physics was to become
the fountainhead of great discoveries on the atom.

Until about 1865 the tradition of physical science at
Cambridge and Oxford was against experimental research.
Physics was taught by mathematicians who had no experience in laboratory experimentation, and who saw little
value in teaching the art to their pupils. But at about this
time, when world trade and manufacture requiring techno-
logical know-how was developing rapidly, many young
people had to be trained in technical skills to qualify them
for a variety of business enterprises. This type of training
included laboratory research. 'J.J.,' writes Thomson's son,
'was of the first generation to be taught physics as a practical
subject.'

In 1870, the seventh Duke of Devonshire, himself a
mathematician, offered to pay for a laboratory and appara-

tus to be set up in Cambridge. In grateful recognition of the gift, the laboratory was named Cavendish after the Duke's family name. History was to show that no money was ever better spent.

For thirty-four years, Thomson was Cavendish Professor of Experimental Physics, and later became the director of the Laboratory. During this time he trained hundreds of scientists who achieved world distinction. Besides himself, eight of his pupils, some of whom are part of our story, received the Nobel Prize.

Joseph John Thomson, of Scotch descent, was born in Cheetham, near Manchester, on December 18, 1856. His father, Joseph James Thomson was a bookseller and publisher carrying on the family tradition of dealing in rare and antique books. It is said that J. J., as Thomson was affectionately called by everyone including his son, acquired from his father his taste for picking up old books on market place stalls. J. J.'s mother, Emma Thomson, was described by a cousin as 'a small lady with bright dark eyes, beaming with kindness. She wore her hair in clusters of ringlets,' in the style of a female character in a Dickens novel. Her nephews and nieces remembered her for the annual parties she gave them after a pantomime outing. When the performance was over, the children were driven home in a four-wheeled horse cab, called a 'growler,' and given a lavish high tea.

A relative of the family recalls J. J. at eleven as 'a small boy in a little grey suit and a blue silk tie, sitting on a rather high chair, with his legs dangling – very silent – and no doubt shy. . . I remember going to tea there once, when Mrs. Thomson said to her son, 'Joe, give your arm to Gertie, and bring her in,' to his embarrassment I thought, for he stumbled over a footstool, and we both nearly came to grief. It was an incident I have always remembered! He must have been in his early teens and very shy.'

Those who look for early signs of a 'bent for science' or

'science in the family' will find little to go by in J. J.'s background. Thomson's own story was that one of his uncles was
interested in meteorology and botany, and that one of his
mother's cousins was secretary of the Manchester Literary
and Philosophical Society. His father had introduced him
to James Prescott Joule, the physicist, and told him that
some day he would be proud to say that he had met him,
which actually came about.

Apparently young Joe was a studious boy. His mother
found him so absorbed that he wasn't much use with work
around the house; she could depend much more on his less
absent-minded brother, Frederick Vernon, younger by two
years. J. J. was an avid reader of the 'yellow-back novels',
forerunners of the modern detective stories. He also sang
music-hall ditties, the 'popular songs' of his day.

J. J.'s parents wanted him to be an engineer, but at fourteen he was too young to become an apprentice, so they sent
him to Owens College (now the University of Manchester)
for preparatory scientific training. In 1873, two years after
J. J. entered Owens College, his father died. Mr. Thomson's
death left his widow with insufficient means to pay the fee
of an engineering firm for J. J.'s apprenticeship. Friends of
the family advised Mrs. Thomson to keep her older son in
college, and thought enough of the family to give them
financial help. Still it was impossible for both sons to attend
college, and so Frederick chose a different calling, going
into business with calico merchants.

J. J. remained in Owens College for five years until he
completed the course in engineering, graduating at the age
of nineteen. During his first two years at Owens, the College
was housed in attic rooms of an old house. There were only
about a half dozen students in physics, under the brilliant
Professor Balfour Stewart, who discovered the law that a
body absorbs the same kind of radiation (light or heat) as it
emits.

The close quarters helped to bring the small group of

students into informal relationship with their exceptional teachers. Toward the end of his life Thomson wrote: 'The teaching I got at Owens College sixty-three years ago was as good as I could get anywhere if I were beginning my studies now. My first introduction to Physics was the lectures of Balfour Stewart. These were so clear that, child as I was, I could understand them.' In turn, Professor Stewart considered Thomson his best and most promising pupil, and used him as his assistant in original experiments. On one such occasion, when the two were trying to find out what happens to mass (weight) during chemical change, the tube in which they heated a mixture of mercury and iodine burst, seriously hurting J. J.'s eyes, and nearly blinding him. From the same professor the serious but happy and friendly student learned not only laboratory methods but also to appreciate the importance of theory in science.

J. J. had received an engineering scholarship and, in 1874, also one in mathematics. Before he left college, he published his first paper on 'Contact Electricity of Insulators'. Upon graduation he again earned a scholarship which enabled him to go to Trinity College, Cambridge, where he remained for the rest of his life.

Thanks to his scholarship, J. J. enjoyed the social privilege and favorable conditions for study in the scholarly atmosphere of Cambridge available only to the sons of the wealthy. As an undergraduate, he preferred private lodgings because in the college there was no one to keep up the fire. His attentive landlady took care of it for him, which was a great help, since, absorbed in work, he invariably forgot to do it himself.

Slight of stature, bony and pale, Thomson was not the college sportsman of his day. He didn't row, play either cricket or football, but took keen enjoyment in watching both cricket and Rugby. In summer, he played lawn tennis, and in winter he walked – often many miles as part of a regular afternoon stint in exercise, referred to as a 'grind.'

On free evenings he played whist, a game resembling bridge.

Enrolled for a higher degree in science, J. J. was required to study mathematics intensively and to prepare for the Mathematical Tripos, a competitive examination. For three years he studied for this examination, placing himself under the direction of a tutor, who had successfully prepared twenty-seven Senior Wranglers (winners of first place). J. J. was not particularly good at such examinations. He couldn't write quickly, judging poorly the amount of time required to answer each question. Since the outcome depended on the maximum number of answers in the minimum time, J. J. came out second, despite the excellent coaching he had received.

After taking the examination in 1880, he turned to a problem dealing with the behavior of cathode (negatively charged) rays. He concluded from his results that an electrified sphere would have its effective mass increased by electrification. This was probably the first hint of connection between energy and mass, a fact which eventually led to the discovery by Einstein that mass and energy are equivalent. J. G. Crowther, a modern British physicist, commenting on this paper says: 'Thomson's remarkable paper of 1881, written when he was twenty-four years old, was like a perfect answer to a super-Tripos question. It was extremely clear, concise, powerful and elegant. . . . It exhibited the genius and the limitations of the Tripos mathematical athleticism.'

By this time, Thomson's ability received enough recognition to secure his election to a fellowship at the college. This meant that he would have enough leisure to conduct research for the next seven years. Immediately after taking his degree J. J. began to work in the Cavendish Laboratory.

During this time he also took on private pupils in mathematics. While most of them were not promising mathematicians, some of the men later achieved distinction. Thomson enjoyed teaching, taking much interest in the personal abilities and peculiarites of the indivdual pupils, a quality which endeared him to the many students he was to have during his long teaching career.

Thomson's early work was in mathematics and in theoretical, rather than experimental, physics. What experimental work he did as a younger man is not considered outstanding. Being 'pathetically helpless with his hands,' he was not very adept at handling apparatus. He usually worked with assistants who did much of the manipulatory work. On the centenary of Thomson's birth, his son wrote: 'In many ways J. J. was a man of paradox. Although he was a great experimentalist with a remarkable power of diagnosing the diseases of a piece of apparatus, he was very clumsy with his hands – except indeed in penmanship, his handwriting being both clear and forceful. In designing apparatus he always used the simplest means and had, I think, no great love of apparatus for its own sake.'

One of his young assistants, himself a noted scientist, also wrote about his master's amazing ability to plan apparatus as well as the experiment, recognize at a glance why it wouldn't work on occasion, how to remove the trouble, all without handling the instrument himself. 'J. J. had a genius for this sort of thing.' This makes his later achievements in experimental physics all the more remarkable.

When, in 1884, a vacancy occurred in the post of Cavendish Professorship, J. J. at the age of twenty-eight was chosen, much older men, with more experimental work to their credit, being passed over. Among the many letters he received on his appointment to the professorship, one from G. F. Fitzgerald of Trinity College, Dublin, said: 'I was very much afraid that they might appoint one of the senior candidates. . . . Although I would of course have liked to be myself appointed, I think the electors have done very much better in appointing you.' In the same year he was elected a Fellow of the Royal Society.

As Professor, he lectured and also directed research.

Among his students were quite a few women. At that time there was a good deal of agitation about whether women should be granted university privileges at all, and J. J. shared in the prevailing view that somehow women could not meet the challenge of a university education. In one letter he wrote:

> I think you would be amused if you were here now to see my lectures – in my elementary one I have got a front row entirely consisting of young women – but the most extraordinary thing is that I have got one at my advanced lecture. I am afraid she does not understand a word and my theory is that she is attending my lectures on the supposition that they are on Divinity and she has not yet found out her mistake.

Only four years later, the young lady referred to was Senior Wrangler.

Shortly after his appointment as Cavendish Professor, Thomson was dining with Sir George and Lady Paget, and became acquainted with their daughter Rose. His host was Regius Professor of Physic (Medicine) at the University. Miss Rose Paget followed her father's interest in science, had some knowledge of mathematics, and took the Higher Local Examination. In 1887 she attended the elementary lectures and demonstrations at the Cavendish Laboratory, and the following year the more advanced demonstrations in Thomson's class.

By 1889, she was doing research on soap films, and J. J. sought occasions to help her with her problems. During these sessions they became good friends, and on one of those days, J. J. asked Rose to marry him. A few weeks later (January 2, 1890) they were married at Little St. Mary's Church. After a brief wedding trip and a visit to J. J.'s mother, they set up their home in one of the houses that belonged to Caius College.

Their home soon became the social center for workers in the Cavendish Laboratory, with Mrs. Thomson having 'at homes' on Saturday afternoons and Sundays. On Sunday evenings J. J. followed the university tradition of dining in Hall at Trinity. At these gatherings of the fellows, there was informal 'shop talk' relating to new experiments, apparatus, and the like.

Several years later, J. J. was responsible for setting up the Cavendish Physical Society, which was more like an institution than an organization, for there were no list of members, dues, or publications. It met every other Tuesday during term time, in the lecture room of the Cavendish Laboratory, with the Professor acting as informal chairman. The idea was not only novel, but so strange that some of the scientists at first refused to attend. Since then the idea of such gatherings has spread to the continent where this type of meeting is called a colloquium, meaning disputation. In American universities it is generally called a seminar, to which any interested person may come to listen to an, as yet, unpublished paper read by a member of the department or laboratory. It is a sort of testing-ground for the reader of the paper, where he is likely to receive constructive criticism from a senior member, while for other research workers and students it offers the opportunity of becoming acquainted with 'what is cooking' in the laboratory.

It was customary for Mrs. Thomson, with the help of some other ladies, to serve tea before these meetings. J. J. was a bit concerned lest the meeting should degenerate into just a social function: his way of guarding against it was to insist that the tea be served in the plainest possible cups and saucers. After tea, the paper was read, the subject having been announced through a note sent around to the laboratory. Sometimes a visitor was invited to read a paper or to demonstrate a new experiment. General discussion followed the presentation, which not only stimulated interest, but sharpened the critical ability of the younger scientists.

When an important discovery came under discussion the meeting room was filled to overflowing. On one such occasion, in 1895, the announcement of Roentgen's discovery of X-rays drew a tremendous audience.

Certain discoveries are important not only in themselves, but for the impetus they give to other research. This was true of the exciting X-rays, the remarkable properties of which engaged the attention of workers in many laboratories, but particularly at Cambridge. Another event responsible for a great outburst of activity in the Cavendish Laboratory, marking the beginning of a new scientific epoch, was the sudden influx of post-graduate students from other universities.

In 1895, the Senate (a body similar to a board of trustees) ruled that Cambridge should open its doors to graduates from outside, and award a degree after two years' residence and the presentation of an approved thesis. At about the same time, a number of research scholarships, known as Exhibition of 1851 Scholarships, were founded. The Prince Consort had organized the Great Exhibition, the profits from which were to be devoted to education. The commissioners of this fund were charged with administering the moneys that accrued from the exhibition and which were invested in land at South Kensington. Promising students from Ireland, Canada, Australia, New Zealand, and South Africa, elected by their own universities, were invited to Cambridge on a scholarship of 150 pounds a year. (Among the first arrivals was Ernest Rutherford, discoverer of the atomic nucleus.)

The granting of these awards initiated what was then known as the Research Student Movement, which was however, for various reasons, unwelcome in certain quarters. Some Cambridge students, whose parents had paid the full fee, felt that these outsiders were admitted on 'cheap terms' and were, in a sense, trespassers depreciating the value of their own degrees. Furthermore, these men, who had been

chosen because of their ability, were competitors for fellowships and other desirable appointments, to say nothing of
their competing for the limited facilities and meager apparatus for which the Cavendish Laboratory was noted – as
well as for the attention of the professor. The last of these
was perhaps the least justified fear on the part of the 'native'
students, because the warm interest, understanding, and
sympathetic help so generously extended by Professor
Thomson included all who came under his direction.

Despite the mutterings that the Research Students were
'not Cambridge men,' J. J., by his actions, let every one
know that he welcomed the newcomers, helping them to
adapt to Cambridge traditions and ways of life, to find their
place in the Cavendish family, and to attain fellowships if
they merited them. The foreign students, in turn, were
grateful for his watchful interest in their welfare. Once the
barriers were broken, and all were welded into one Cambridge School, rich rewards were reaped from this gathering
of brilliant young physicists. Year after year young scientists
with exceptional ability arrived from overseas with the
single purpose of doing research. For many years, no greater
team of research scientists could have been found anywhere
working together under one roof than the one in Cambridge.

At thirty-eight, J. J. had been Cavendish Professor for
ten years, had organized the work of the laboratory, taught
and directed the work of many students, had done considerable work on the discharge of electricity through gases and
had written two important books: *Applications of Dynamics
to Physics and Chemistry* (1888), and *Recent Researches in
Electricity and Magnetism* (1893); yet he was still to make
his major contribution.

IN 1895, the conditions could not have been more favorable
for Thomson's great discovery: there was the laboratory,
his ten-year experience with discharge of electricity in gases,
the best of co-workers, and the newly discovered X-rays.

J. J. invited Rutherford, recent arrival from New Zealand, to work with him on the effect of X-rays on gases.

By this time Thomson, like others, had observed cathode rays inside what is called a *gas discharge tube*. This is simply a glass tube into which a pair of metal electrodes has been sealed, one at each end. When the discharge tube operates at a high voltage, after the air is pumped out of the tube, leaving almost a vacuum, a beam of rays leaps the gap between the two plates. At *very* low pressures, the intensity of the light in the tube diminishes, and a green fluorescent glow in the tube walls appears. This glow is produced by something emanating from the negative electrode or cathode. Though invisible, the rays cause the fluorescence to appear when they strike glass or other objects inside the tube.

It was with this type of evacuated tube that Wilhelm Konrad Roentgen discovered X-rays. One day when he turned on a cathode-ray tube, he noticed that a near-by piece of paper coated with barium platinocyanide (a fluorescent chemical) glowed with a greenish-blue light. He knew that the cathode rays themselves could not escape. By putting objects between the tube and the paper he found that some *new* kind of ray was coming from the tube. These rays not only caused certain substances to fluoresce, but penetrated paper, glass, thick pieces of wood, and even metal. By cable and wire, the news of these amazing rays went round the world.

Where did the remarkable rays come from? When the negative terminal or cathode of a vacuum tube is heated by an electric current so that it glows white hot, it gives off a stream of electrons or 'cathode rays' which move toward the anode with extremely high speed. In an X-ray tube, the anode is a 'target,' usually made of tungsten, a metal which can withstand great heat without melting. Under a very high voltage, electrons loosened from the cathode are hurled with great force against the tungsten plate. X-rays thus

8. *Marie Curie with her daughters, Eve and Irène from left to right.*

9. *Marie Curie with Dean Pegram in the United States in* 1921.

bounce off from the metal of the target. X-rays are radiations of very short wave length, which means that their frequency is very high. The higher the frequency the greater their energy and penetrating power.

Thomson and Rutherford got to work at once on other effects of these powerful rays. They showed that X-rays released charged ions in a gas. In other words, these rays possessed the property to *ionize* air or other gases through which they passed, to disturb the gas molecules so violently that some were broken into charged fragments or ions. The stream of ions could be deflected by an electric force or magnet.

As valuable as the discovery of X-rays was to become in medicine, surgery, dentistry, and industry, it was even more important for its stimulating effect on the study of atomic structure. Among the first to contribute to our knowledge of the 'universe' inside the atom, was J. J. Thomson, the discoverer of the *electron*. First came the proof that cathode rays are made up of particles. (These are the beta particles.)

If a small screen coated with zinc sulfide is placed in the path of the cathode rays inside the tube, the zinc sulfide lights up when the current is turned on. The glow can be seen as tiny bursts of light, with each unit that strikes the screen. The bursts of light are all of the same size, each particle of zinc sulfide hit by a unit charge giving off a flash of light.

Next came the proof that these unit particles are charged. If a magnet is placed outside the tube, the narrow stream and its glowing spot on the screen shift to the right or to the left depending on which way the magnet is held. The fact that the rays can be deflected by a magnet shows that the stream is charged. The last and most important fact: the charged particles can be 'weighed!' J. J. succeeded in doing this, too.

The 'weighing' was done with the magnet, for no scale so sensitive as to weigh electrons has yet been devised. The principle Thomson employed was as simple as it was ingenious. The heavier the particles, the more will it take to deflect the stream, he reasoned; the stronger the magnet, the farther will the stream be deflected. By measuring the magnetic force needed to deflect the beam of particles he was able to measure their mass, indirectly, that is in relation to their charge.

J. J. discovered that the particles were much lighter than anything that was yet known, far lighter than the hydrogen atom, the lightest element. These units of current 'weighed' only 1/1840 as much as a single atom of hydrogen. Thus J. J. Thomson wrenched a unit of matter from the atom, a particle 1,840 times smaller than the tiniest atom, and one which carried a unit charge of electricity. To these particles he gave the name *electrons*. When an electric current flows, it is the electrons that flow.

All electrons are alike, no matter what material is used in the cathode; their mass and charge are always the same, even though their speed and number may differ with the substance from which they are emitted. Having discovered the electron, J. J. also grasped the full meaning that this had for the structure of the atom. The atom, in whatever kind of matter, he explained, formerly thought to be indivisible, had been split, tiny pieces having been stripped from it.

In 1897, Thomson described his experiments on the electron to the Royal Institution, an audience of eminent physicists, most of whom were exceedingly skeptical about the soundness of Thomson's ideas of matter. 'Opposition to the idea of particles smaller than atoms did indeed continue, but it was merely the spasmodic dying kicks of the older physics, a matter of muscular contraction rather than brain,' writes his son. But J. J. didn't falter in following up his correct idea.

In the next three or four years, over a hundred original papers were published on the work in the Cavendish Laboratory. In 1903, J. J. Thomson published his book, *Con-duction of Electricity Through Gases,* which included the reports of the research done during this brilliant period. J. G. Crowther tells us that when some twenty research workers, scattered in groups of two or three, were working on some problem each had 'chosen from a multitude in the air or had adopted at the professor's suggestion. . . . Nearly all of the gifted young men were working on some aspect of the grand scheme of research into the constitution of matter and electricity which existed in J. J.'s head.'

In 1906, the Nobel Prize in Physics went to J. J. Thomson 'In recognition of the great merits of his theoretical and experimental researches on the discharge of electricity through gases.' The day after the lavish banquet, J. J. delivered his Nobel lecture on the 'Carriers of Negative Electricity' before the Royal Academy of Sciences. Finally, the laureates were entertained at dinner by the King of Sweden.

To his brother, J. J. wrote:

> Dear Fred:
>
> Very many thanks for your kind letter of congratulations. I am very glad to have the prize not only because it is a very substantial sum of money, but because it is a testimony to my work from foreigners who are entire strangers to me and could not have been influenced by personal considerations. It is gratifying that in the three years the prize for Physics has twice been given to an Englishman. We are busy this term at the laboratory and I shall soon have the building of the extension of it on my hands. . . .

THOMSON was to make still another major contribution that was important for the development of atomic energy. He decided to investigate the positive rays coming from the anode. He designed a tube with a thick cathode with a hole drilled in its center, hoping to catch the positive rays in a straight beam as they passed through the hole. Outside the cathode end of the tube he placed a photographic plate. When the current was turned on, the stream of particles passed through the hole and on to the photographic plate, making a little black spot, the diameter of the beam.

The next step was to measure their mass by the same method he had used a number of years before to 'weigh' the electron. A powerful magnet placed near the tube diverted the charged particles from their straight path. The black spot on the photographic plate shifted with the bending of the rays. Reasoning as before, the heavier particles should be deflected less than the lighter ones. Furthermore, if there were more than one particle size, there should be several spots – wherever each hit the plate.

The gas Thomson studied was neon, the one used in neon signs. When the positive rays streaming out of the tube hit the plate off center, they formed a spot corresponding to a mass of 20, which was what he expected, for the atomic weight of this inert gas is 20.18. But more exciting was the appearance of a fine shadow close to it, which corresponded to a weight of 22. What did this mean? Could it be that there were *two* kinds of neon, one with an atomic weight of 20 and one with 22? It must be that neon gas existed in two forms, the same element with different atomic weights. Since the atomic weight of the mixture was closer to 20 than to 22, the heavier one was present in smaller amounts.

Elements that have the same atomic number (some multiple of hydrogen) but differing atomic weights are called *isotopes*. Neon had two isotopes. The separation of the isotopes of uranium was an essential part in the preparation of the material used in the release of atomic energy.

In 1908, J. J. Thomson was made Knight (Knight Bachelor) conferring upon him the title 'Sir,' and four years later he received the Order of Merit. But not only his own government honored him. He received honorary doctorate degrees from more than twenty universities in the Dominion and from the Sorbonne, Columbia, Philadelphia, Göttingen, and Cracow. He was elected to honorary membership in twice as many learned societies in England and in other parts of the world. In addition to the medals he received from learned societies and institutes, there were two from the Worshipful Company of Salters, and the Worshipful Company of Grocers.

In 1915 he was elected president of the Royal Society and served for five years. In 1918, he accepted the Mastership of Trinity College, resigning from the Cavendish chair the next year. This ended his active leadership of the laboratory, but through the creation of a special professorship, his connection with it continued. J. J. was then sixty-three, and while his time of creative experimentation was over, his interest in physics, and his daily visits to the laboratory continued almost uninterrupted.

A great man is judged by the importance of the work he leaves behind. By this measure alone, Thomson belongs among the world's great scientists. His published works numbered over 250, including eleven books, one of which was written with his son George Paget, also a physicist of Nobel Prize fame. But one of his greatest contributions was the one which Cavendish Laboratory made to our age of electronics. Apart from the contributions to theory, the hundreds of new devices, instruments, and whole industries built around the electron are a monument to the institution which he directed for thirty-four years.

A startling point of contrast between this contribution, and the total cost of research equipment at the laboratory during these years is often made. It is said that only 10,000 pounds was spent on apparatus during J. J.'s directorship. Apparently it was an idiosyncracy of J. J.'s to be overly careful when it came to spending money for apparatus. For years Cavendish men struggled with antiquated electrometers and other basic equipment. One time he insisted that the laboratory could not afford the price (5 pounds) for a new electroscope designed by Curie. The story is told that when a research worker gathered his apparatus for a new experiment, he had to carry a drawn sword in one hand and his apparatus, or rather somebody else's in the other. A maxim attributed to J. J. was that 'the most useful instrument a laboratory can have is a good balance in the bank.'

This stringency in spending characterized also the handling of his personal money affairs. Apart from the Nobel Prize, which was then worth about 7,000 pounds, he received no large gifts, salaries, or fees. Yet he amassed a personal fortune of 82,000 pounds. The extent of his fortune, derived largely from skillful operations in the Stock Exchange, was not known until after his death. Perhaps this is a reflection of his background – a family of shrewd and thrifty business men. He lived most modestly, and his social as well as professional life centered around the laboratory and university.

His cultural interests were simple. He did not enjoy classical concerts, preferring Gilbert and Sullivan operas. In addition to thrillers, of which he read a great many, he liked Dickens, Scott, George Eliot, and Jane Austen. He loved Cambridge, its setting and climate, and engaged in the simple but vigorous activities of long country walks, and 'he would vault over gates and stiles.' J. G. Crowther has said that he probably played Rugby in his head, in the same way as he saw the plan and strategy of an experiment 'in his mind's eye.' His hobbies were gardening, classifying of wild flowers, and book-collecting from second-hand shops.

Most of all he loved people, particularly his students. 'He probably preferred the company of the ordinary student to that of the intellectual.' He was more interested in their personal idiosyncracies and amusements than in their work, 'often engaging in personal discussion and gossip rather than philosophical conversation.' The fact that he did not feel too 'superior' to converse with anyone is revealed by a

letter to his son. On the occasion of one of his visits to the
United States to give a series of lectures at Yale, he wrote:

> The son of one of the Professors here who is only seven
> years old wanted to attend my lectures, but was told that
> he would not understand them. I met him and had a talk
> with him one afternoon. When I had gone he told his
> mother he thought it was a great shame he had not been
> allowed to go to lectures for he had a talk with Professor
> Thomson and could understand what he said as well as
> he could anyone else.

At the age of seventy-seven he was still youthful in body
and spirit. His biographer, a former pupil, and the son of
Thomson's predecessor at Cavendish, tells a story of J. J.'s
Atlantic cruise in 1933, with his daughter Joan (Mrs. Thomson was too ill to leave England):

> At Madeira he was disappointed to find that toboggan-
> ing was less sensational than he had been led to expect. He
> insisted on going about in a bullock cart rather than a
> taxi. In the last two summer holidays he went for motor
> tours with his daughter. He was delighted with the hotel
> waiter at Stratford-on-Avon, who, after helping Miss
> Thomson to what remained on the dish, said, 'I will bring
> some more for your husband, madam.'

Six weeks before he died, his daughter was describing
some wild flowers she had seen while riding, but could not
remember a particular one. From her discription he gave
her the name immediately.

J. J. died on August 30, 1940, at the age of eighty-four.
After cremation, the funeral was held in Westminster
Abbey, in the nave where lie the remains of Newton, Dar-
win, Kelvin, and J. J.'s pupil and co-worker, Ernest
Rutherford.

> About his scientific contribution, Professor W. L. Bragg,
> a pupil of J. J.'s, wrote: 'He more than any other man,

was responsible for the fundamental change in outlook
which distinguishes the physics of this century from that
of the last.' Professor G. M. Trevelyan, his friend and
successor at Trinity College, said he will be remembered
for '. . . his unaffected modesty, the most beautiful of all
settings for superlative powers of mind; his ever-active
love of the College; his interests in its athletic as well as its
academic successes and failures from day to day; his evident desire to be regarded as an ordinary plain man
among ordinary plain men, though his genius had in fact
raised him so high above our heads.'

ERNEST RUTHERFORD
(1871–1937)

. . . and Now the Nucleus

ONE SUMMER DAY during vacation from school (when Rutherford was digging potatoes on his father's farm in New Zealand), his mother came to tell him the glad news that he was granted the Exhibition 1851 Scholarship to Cambridge. He threw his spade aside and said: 'That's the last potato I'll dig.' It was 1895, and Ernest Rutherford was twenty-four years old, a graduate of Canterbury College, Christchurch, New Zealand. The records of the 1851 Royal Commission state that the award was made to Rutherford whose 'theses cover a very wide extent of experimental work on Magnetism and Electricity.'

Ernest Rutherford was born on August 30, 1871, at Brightwater in South Island, New Zealand, only twenty-nine years after the first English settlers had come to the island. Ernest's grandfather, George Rutherford, a wheelwright from Perth, Scotland was engaged in 1842 to construct a sawmill in New Zealand where he settled with his family. One of his sons, James, was later to become Ernest's father, marrying Martha Thompson, whose family had also taken the long journey from England. Ernest's father, like his grandfather, was a wheelwright, which meant that he had a skill that could easily be turned to other pursuits. He earned his living by bridge-building and other construction work required in establishing a railway in the newly developing country. In addition, like many of the settlers, he carried on small-scale farming, one of the crops being flax for the making of linen. Ernest's mother was a teacher. She played the piano, and looked after her family of seven sons and five daughters. Ernest was their fourth child and second son.

James Rutherford was industrious, competent, and versatile. In his flax-milling operations he harnessed water-power to drive the mill. He experimented with different methods of soaking the flax, planted selected native varieties; his product was considered the best in the Dominion. He also developed a specal labor-saving device for the scraping of the flax fiber. Mrs. Rutherford helped with the farm as well as with the education of their children.

Ernest enjoyed the advantage that a large happy family provides in the way of wholesome discipline — sharing the responsibilities of the home. He was accustomed to doing chores around the farm: wood chopping, gardening, helping to milk cows, and running errands. Still, there was time for play, in which he engaged as most normal young boys do. He also had hobbies. Imitating his father, he made model water-wheels, snapped pictures with a home-made camera, and took clocks apart. Like his mother, he liked to sing and read, especially Dickens. On holidays, he swam, rode horseback, fished for trout, speared eels, feasted on berries, and shot wild pigeons.

His parents valued education, as did the entire community of vigorous and pioneering settlers, for they appropriated an unusually large sum for schools; by 1885 the community had set up Nelson College. Ernest was sent to primary school

when he was five, and his family, at the cost of many comforts, maintained him through a university education.
Years later, at a social function, Rutherford remarked: 'I
should never have been where I am today if it wasn't for my
mother and father.'

He was fortunate also in his teachers (beginning with his
mother). As a result he received a sound and well-rounded
education. A science text-book which he used when he was
ten, written by Balfour Stewart (J. J. Thomson's science
teacher in Manchester), gave him his start in science. The
book was intended, states the author in the preface, not only
to give information 'but to discipline the mind for which
purpose a series of simple experiments are described.' Those
who knew him well said that the influence of this book
could be traced in Rutherford's later thinking and experimenting. Mathematics was Ernest's strong subject, but he
received scholarships and prizes also in Latin, French, English literature, history, physics, and chemistry.

In 1882, the family moved to Havelock, a village east
of Nelson, where James Rutherford erected a flax-mill for
making into fibre the wild flax that grew in the neighboring
swamps, and a water-driven sawmill for cutting railway
sleepers, for which he had received a large contract. Ernest
attended the Havelock school until he was fifteen, when he
competed for a county scholarship to Nelson College, worth
fifty guineas a year. While parents and neighbors were peep-
ing into the examination room to see how the contestants
were doing, Ernest won 580 marks out of 600, and the
scholarship.

It was at Nelson College that he won prizes in a wide
variety of subjects, and, in his last year, gained a scholarship
to the New Zealand University, being fourth in a list of ten.
In 1890 he entered Canterbury College (of the University).
When, two years later, the senior university scholarships
were awarded, Rutherford received the one in mathematics.
It was only at this time that he began to show real promise

in physics. Up to 1892, though he had shown himself to be an excellent scholar in other subjects, his real talent, which was in science, had only begun to bear fruit. By the time he graduated from the university, his abilities in science earned him the first honors in mathematics and physics. His late start in the speciality in which he was to become one of the immortal great, perhaps accounted for his wide if not intensive knowledge in a great many other fields. Rutherford was considered a generally well-informed, though not sophisticated man.

A fellow undergraduate wrote about him: 'Rutherford was a boyish, frank, simple and very likeable youth with no precocious genius, but when once he saw his goal he went straight to the central point.'

During his last two years at the University he became deeply absorbed in experiments in magnetization of iron, which led to his invention of a magnetic detector of radio waves. In the 'miserable, cold, draughty, concrete-floored cellar, which was usually known to students as the 'den' and in which they were accustomed to hang up their caps and gowns,' he carried on a variety of ingenious experiments. His reading included the work of Faraday, J. J. Thompson, and others with whose work he became thoroughly familiar. His thesis on the 'Magnetization of Iron by High-Frequency Discharges' was read before the Philosophical Institute.

Having applied for the scholarship for Cambridge, he went back after graduation for another year to Canterbury College, since the awards were made only every other year. During his university days, Rutherford lodged with Mrs. De Renzy Newton, a widow with four children. There he became acquainted with Mrs. Newton's oldest daughter, Mary; they saw a great deal of each other, Mary visiting with the Rutherfords on many holidays. Before he went to Cambridge they became engaged. We learn much about his life at the Cavendish Laboratory through his letters to Mary Newton.

IN THE FALL of 1895, Rutherford started out from New Zealand for Cambridge, borrowing money for his passage. He was detained in London by a brief illness. While there, he received a warm letter from J. J. explaining the new system of Research Student scholarships and inviting him to Cambridge for a personal interview. This was to be the beginning of a great friendship and mutually profitable collaboration.

The first research student to arrive at Cavendish, he was welcomed by Professor Thomson, and taken under his wing. His fame, thanks partly to his novel detector, spread among the younger men, who were at first prepared to ignore him as an unwelcome intruder. It didn't take long for Rutherford to gain their respect and admiration. In the words of Dr. Andrew Balfour: 'We've got a rabbit here from the Antipodes and he's burrowing mighty deep.'

The Thomsons extended the hospitality of their home to him, inviting him to dinner, while Mrs. Thomson found comfortable lodgings for him. Some months later Ernest wrote to Mary:

> Mrs. J. J. told anyone she got a chance that they must go to see the wonderful experiment of Mr. Rutherford. . . . It is lucky I am of a modest disposition, but these things do not affect me in the way you might expect. I really think Mrs. J. J. regards me with considerable favour for several reasons. She always introduces me as Mr. . . . who has come all the way from New Zealand. I think she appreciates the compliment to her husband by my coming straight from New Zealand to the Cavendish. . . .

Apparently, J. J. himself thought a good deal of Rutherford's ability, for in November of that year in a letter to Mary, Rutherford said:

> You have heard me talk of the Physical Society, J. J.'s pet society. Well, he has asked me to give an account of

some of my work before it, and I am to occupy the whole meeting. I am to show some experiments for the interest of the vulgar. Usually it is only well-known people, Profs and such like, who shine before the society, so I appreciate the honour of being asked. It is my chance of getting a little lift up on the scientific ladder, and I intend to make as good use of it as possible. Among so many scientific bugs knocking about one has a little difficulty in rising to the front, and naturally I am very pleased at having the opportunity of asserting myself. You mustn't think I am egotistical ·in talking like this, but the sooner I rise up the sooner I will get a decent appointment and the sooner. . . .

The unfinished sentence told Mary a great deal. Rutherford was looking forward to the time when he would have the means to get married. In the meantime, J. J. found odd jobs for him — book reviewing, lecturing, and giving examinations, while Rutherford tried to cover his living expenses, and pay off the debt — the money he had borrowed for his passage to England.

His first work at the laboratory was to extend the range of his detector, increasing it to half a mile, proving that electro-magnetic waves travelled this distance from transmitter to receiver, and even through brick walls. His detector was indeed a great success, which amazed all who saw the demonstration, but not the demonstrator who fully expected that it would work. He had written Mary that the detector had great practical importance. 'If I could get an appreciable effect at 10 miles I would probably be able to make a considerable amount of money out of it,' he wrote her. But the urge to make money soon gave way to his much greater interest in science.

When the discovery of X-rays was announced in November 1895, their power to produce an image of the skeleton through living tissue intrigued young and old among the laboratory workers. Everyone including Rutherford was

stimulated to work with the new rays. When J. J. asked
him to work with him, Rutherford forever set aside his own
work and was happy to join him. He admired J. J. and he
also saw the tremendous scientific significance in exploring
the nature of X-rays. A number of important results came
out of these experiments: they found that the longer the
column of gas that was exposed to X-rays, the greater its
conductivity – an effect opposite to that seen in a copper
wire; X-rayed gases lost their conductivity when blown
through porous plugs; the gas could take up only a certain
amount of current, and once saturated, regardless of how
high the voltage, it could not take up any more current.

These effects fitted into the theory that the X-rays produced a definite quantity of positive and negative ions in
the gas. A number of calculations could be made from these
facts: the number of ions, the size of their electric charge,
the rate at which they flowed in opposite directions toward
the cathode and anode, and the size of the saturation current. At the end of that year, they reported their results
before the Meeting of the British Association.

In this work with particles Rutherford displayed a confidence in his results which could not fail to gain him recognition from his peers. One day when he was giving his
demonstration before the British Association his apparatus
failed. Unperturbed, he looked up at the audience and said,
'Something has gone wrong! If you would all like to go for
a stroll and a smoke for five minutes, it will be working on
your return.' His listeners were delighted to have the inter-
mission, and returned shortly to see the experiment work.
A leading physicist commented: 'That young man will go
a long way.' Not only was he at home with his apparatus, but
the material he was working with seemed to be a part of
him. He was known to remark: 'Ions are jolly little beggars;
you can almost see them.'

Rutherford continued with this work, showing not only
what happens in a conducting gas, but how to *measure*

these effects. It is like the difference between knowing that water can be pushed up hill, and predicting the amount of force it will require to push a definite quantity of water to a certain level in a column of a given diameter.

Using the same methods, Rutherford next became interested in other forms of radiation, the type Becquerel had observed emanating from uranium salts. He found that uranium radiations ionized gases in the same way as X-rays. Having measured their exact penetrating powers in different gases and solids, he discovered that they were absorbed in proportion to the density of the gas.

In the spring of 1897, Mary came to England. The Thomsons invited her to spend May Week with them, and she fully enjoyed their warm hospitality. Mary remained in England for the summer, visiting relatives when Rutherford was occupied in the laboratory. This was the summer when he received his first B. A. Research degree, Mary being present at the Senate House on the occasion. After that, they accompanied two friends to Ireland, visiting Killarney. While in Cambridge they took time out for outings and races on the Cam. In the fall Mary Newton returned to New Zealand.

In December of that year, he wrote her:

> I have a great piece of news to tell you, which you probably have heard about already. I went in for the Coutts Trotter Scholarship, and it has been awarded me for two years at 250 pounds a year, think of it—nearly enough to get married on. I collected together my published papers and sent a short MS. of my unpublished work and calmly awaited the result. . . .

RUTHERFORD'S first major discovery was still to come, and he was to travel to yet another continent to make it. Someone has said that it is rare for a man to have Scotland, New Zealand, Cambridge, *and* Canada in his blood, but it happened to Rutherford, for the opportunity came for him to

10. *Sir J. J. Thomson.*

11. *Ernest (Lord) Rutherford (right) and John Cavendish in the Cavendish Laboratory.*

occupy a research chair in physics in Canada. When a vacancy was created in McGill University in Montreal, the trustees looked around for the best possible man to fill it. J. J. recommended Rutherford, and a representative of the university came to England to interview the applicant.

As much as Thomson would have liked Rutherford to stay on, he urged his brilliant pupil to take the post in Canada, and as eager as Rutherford was to get the professorship, he wrote home that he would not accept the offer unless J. J. advised him to, for such was their great mutual esteem.

On August 3, 1898, he wrote to Mary:

> Rejoice with me my dear girl, for matrimony is looming in the distance. I got word on Monday, from Dr. Peterson, to say I was appointed to Montreal. All my friends are of course very pleased, and I have to submit to being called professor without having a boot to throw at their heads. I am very pleased that it is settled and that I am not left in the cold, but I am sorry for many reasons to leave Cambridge.

A month later, just after his twenty-seventh birthday, he sailed for Canada. The salary was small – 500 pounds – but the laboratory was about the best equipped of its kind in the world, paid for by a tobacco millionaire. Rutherford wrote his fiancée that he was expected 'to form a research school in order to knock the shine out of the Yankees,' and to his mother, that he preferred the Montreal position at 500 to one in New Zealand at 700. He immediately saw better prospects here for research and advancement.

Rutherford lost no time. Within the first few weeks he ordered uranium and thorium salts for the research he planned to do. Within the next fifteen months he worked like a beaver, setting up a research department with four young workers assisting. In their research on radioactivity, they discovered that thorium compounds gave off 'emanations' – radioactive particles which had the power to ionize gases, on any other substances on which they fell. What was the nature of this powerful radiation?

He thought that the radiation the Curies obtained from pitchblende was due to a state of division of the substance 'rather than to the presence of a new and powerful radiating substance.' In this he was completely wrong – perhaps his greatest scientific error – for within a few weeks after he made this statement, the Curies showed the substance to be radium.

He called this radiation ER ('excited radioactivity'), a phenomenon which intrigued him for many years, because he thought he might thus have discovered artificial radioactivity. (By some strange coincidence, its name bore the first initials of his own.) This fanciful ambition he was never to realize. When, about thirty-five years later, the Joliot-Curies achieved it, he sent them his warm congratulations.

In the summer of 1900 he returned to his birthplace and married Mary Newton. They had been engaged for five years, during which time, except for Mary's brief visit in England, they had not seen each other. The couple returned to Canada to settle down in the reasonable comfort that the young husband could now provide for a family. Their daughter Eileen, who was to be their only child, was born the next year.

At about the time of Eileen's birth, there was also a new arrival in the laboratory. Frederick Soddy, a young chemist who had graduated from Oxford, joined Rutherford in his experiments in radioactivity. Their association, though brief, was fruitful. Soddy's training in chemistry was helpful in the study of emanations, for as it turned out, Rutherford's 'emanation' was not a physical radiation but a new chemical atom. They tried all kinds of chemical reagents on this substance to find out what it was like, but it would not react. They believed that it was an inert gas, similar to the argon family, which had been discovered several years before.

What they found was that the radioactivity given off by thorium, 'decayed' and was permanently lost, while the rest of the thorium recovered this property. And the rate of decay of radioactivity of the particles was exactly equal to the rate of recovery of thorium. This discovery, that radioactivity consists of the spontaneous transformation of atoms, was the first major result of Rutherford's research.

Soddy later returned to London, joining William Ramsay with whom he continued to work on radioactive emanations. By this time the Curies had discovered that radium excited radioactivity in neighboring particles, and Becquerel showed that the radioactivity of uranium could be removed chemically. What was true of the recovery by thorium was also true of uranium. It all added up now. Thorium lost its radioactivity because of the loss of radioactive particles. It soon recovered this property as it produced within itself new emanating particles. All of the different radioactive substances behaved according to the same law – the rate of decay was proportional to the amount of radioactive material formed. Together with Ramsay, Soddy separated helium gas from radium, and announced their discovery in 1904. Radium was constantly shooting off helium (alpha) particles, as all other radioactive substances did.

Meanwhile Rutherford continued along another path. Could these radioactive particles be put to use to pry into the interior of the atom? He had already deflected the alpha rays by electric and magnetic fields. They were positively charged, and traveled at a rate of about one-twelfth of that of light. The alpha rays were really atomic fragments hurled out of exploding atoms, like projectiles. The electrons (beta rays) were only incidental to the most important change that was taking place in radioactive matter.

Macdonald, the man who made his money in tobacco, and hated smoking for its 'filthy habit' was induced to furnish funds for a piece of equipment the laboratory lacked. With this machine Rutherford confirmed the earlier hunch that the emanations were inert but radioactive gases. There was no doubt now that radioactivity was a transformation of matter. What was it due to, and how much energy did it take to shoot off these particles? Could the energy inside the atom be calculated from the energies of the alpha particles? The answer was astounding! It must be perhaps a million times as great as the energy in any chemical change, such as the burning of coal.

The arithmetic was plain: according to the rate of energy output, one gram of uranium would, in a million years, lose less than a milligram (one/one thousandth of a gram) of its weight, while a gram of radium would lose about the same amount in one year. Then calculation clearly showed that the time it takes radium to lose half its weight was a few thousand years. This is called its 'half-life,' or just its 'life.'

The conclusion: the energy sealed in the atom must be vast! Further, Rutherford wrote: 'There is no reason to assume that this enormous store of energy is possessed by the radio-elements alone. It seems probable that atomic energy in general is of a similar, high order of magnitude, although the absence of change prevents its existence being manifested. . . .' The measurements of the energy of alpha particles revealed the first truth about the enormity of atomic energy.

Rutherford's exciting results made a great impression in European and American laboratories. During 1903 and 1904 he was invited to give lectures in leading universities in the United States (Yale, California, and Illinois) and in various parts of England. At this time he published his first book, *Radio-activity*. The next year he went to New Zealand, giving lectures and writing papers. From New Zealand he wrote to Mrs. Rutherford: '. . . They are following my trail, and if I am to have a chance for a Nobel Prize in the next few years I must keep my work moving.'

Shortly afterwards Rutherford received a new co-worker from England. On May 20, 1905 Sir William Ramsay wrote from London recommending Dr. Otto Hahn, a German chemist. 'Hahn is a capital fellow,' he wrote, 'and has done his work admirably. I am sure that you would enjoy having him to work with you.' Not intended as such, it was like an exchange of professors – Hahn for Soddy.

While working with Ramsay, Otto Hahn, using Mme. Curie's method of repeated crystallization, had tried to extract radium from thorianite ore. Much to their surprise, though they produced very little radium, the residue became more and more radioactive. Their repeated concentrations led to the discovery of a substance many times more radioactive than the parent thorium. Their experience was similar to that of Mme. Curie when she extracted radium from the pitchblende.

It was at this point that Hahn came with the question: what is this substance? With his poor English he didn't at first get across his enthusiasm to Rutherford. But when Hahn showed him the emanation of thorium which decays to half value in 1.9 years, there was no longer any doubt that the young man had something to back up his enthusiasm. At the end of a year of working with Rutherford, Hahn discovered radioactinium, an important member of the thorium family. Shortly afterwards Hahn returned to Germany, where we will meet him again thirty years later in the story of atom-splitting.

Long afterward Hahn wrote about his McGill days:

Rutherford was so sincere and unassuming in his dealing with his students and with every day things of life, that we two Germans [Hahn and one named Levin] in particular were constantly filled with surprise and admiration. We had no doubt imagined that such a distinguished professor would be an unapproachable person, conscious of his dignity. Nothing could have been further from the truth. I still possess a small photograph which shows him cleaning away the snow from the entrance to his house.

In this house were often evening guests, listening in rapt attention to the intimate piano playing of Mrs. Rutherford or to the spirited narrative of the Professor.

Rutherford was to move on to greater and more wonderful achievements, more than he could have imagined at that time. There were many offers of university posts in the United States, but he rejected them all, because he felt that neither the United States nor Canada had as yet grown to the stature of England in physics. When a vacancy occurred in the ·University of Manchester he accepted it, leaving Montreal in the spring of 1907.

WRITING about Manchester where he had fifteen research workers from at least six countries (three from America), in a very well-equipped laboratory, buzzing with activity:

> I find the students here regard a full professor as little short of Lord God Almighty. It is quite refreshing after the critical attitude of Canadian students. It is always a good thing to feel you are appreciated.

The Rutherfords settled in a comfortable house with a garden, at Withington, about two miles from the laboratory. In October he wrote to his mother:

> I have now been lecturing a month and getting things into shape. I am naturally very busy and as newcomers we shall probably have to do a good deal of dining out. I go to two big dinners this week, one to Mr. Donner—a wealthy merchant here—and one to Professor Schuster, my predecessor who, unlike most professors, is a wealthy man. Everyone is very kind and I am enjoying my life thoroughly. I have a good many outside lectures in hand and give one today at the Manchester Literary and Philosophical Society. I am lecturing later in London at the Royal Institution, at Dublin, and Liverpool, and so will be kept busy. I am giving a special series of lectures on 'radioactivity' which are well attended.

When Rutherford began his work, the University of Manchester had less than 20 milligrams of pure radium bromide, and so he applied for a loan of this material from the Vienna Academy in order to 'investigate in particular:

1) Physical and chemical properties of the emanation
2) Ionization of gases exposed to very intense radiation
3) Final product of transformation of radium.'

Three hundred and fifty milligrams of the radium salt were soon received. Complicated arrangements were made for Ramsay to share in the use of the precious material, as emanations in little tubes locked in containers were dispatched by private messenger back and forth from Manchester to London.

And then to work. Rutherford and his excellent assistant, Dr. Hans Geiger, a German, got busy counting alpha particles, shooting off from radium. One of Rutherford's biographers later said: 'These particles were counted as a boy counts his marbles, or as a policeman numbers people going through a door.' What were they actually counting? Each particle gave off an individual sparkle or a fluorescent screen. Geiger who, according to Rutherford, was 'a demon at the work' would count right through the night. The answer they obtained from this counting was: one gram of radium ejects 34 billion alpha particles every second! The particles became helium atoms, after picking up two electrons which neutralized the positive charge.

This experiment, by which Rutherford, for the first time, detected a single atom was one of the great landmarks in the history of physics. It was another leap in the direction of establishing modern atomic theory. These two discoveries were to lead him a few years later to reveal the structure and its tremendous internal energy. It's no surprise that his discovery should have received the recognition it did. At the end of the summer of 1908, Rutherford received a telegram announcing that he was to be awarded that year's

Nobel Prize in chemistry, 'for his investigations in regard to the decay of elements and the chemistry of radioactive substances.' Shortly afterward, he was also knighted by his government.

Rutherford wrote to Hahn:

> I much appreciate your kind congratulations and wishes on the award. It is of course quite unofficial but between ourselves I have no reason to doubt its correctness. I must confess it was very unexpected and I am very startled at my metamorphosis into a chemist . . . my wife and I are going to Stockholm via Hamburg and Copenhagen to arrive there on the 10th. We shall probably return via Berlin for the express purpose of seeing you.

He goes on to ask him to hold his mail as it is forwarded to Berlin, and to find 'a comfortable hotel handy for looking around Berlin.'

At a dinner given in Rutherford's honor by the University of Manchester in 1909, J. J. paid this tribute to him:

> Professor Rutherford has never received the credit that he should have had for his work at Cambridge in connection with radio-telegraphy in 1895. His success was so great that I have since felt some misgivings that I persuaded him to devote himself to that new department of physics that was opened by the discovery of Roentgen rays. . . .
>
> Of all the services that can be rendered to science the introduction of new ideas is the very greatest. A new idea serves not only to make many people interested, but it starts a great number of new investigations. . . . There is nobody who has tested his ideas with more rigour than has Professor Rutherford. There can be no man who more nearly fulfills the design of the founder of the Nobel Prize than he does.

DURING the next couple of years there were a visit to
Montreal after a meeting of the British Association at
Winnipeg, to the United States where he lectured once
more, this time at Clark University, attendance at the
Radiology Congress* in Brussels, and a tour through Germany. Everywhere, he was the great figure who dominated
atomic science of his day. There were other awards, honors,
and medals including one from the National Academy of
Sciences in the United States. Dr. Nicholas Murray Butler,
then president of Columbia University, brought the medal
to England, and presented it in person.

Rutherford didn't rest on his laurels. Another epoch-
making event, his crowning achievement, was in the making. From a number of his letters and papers it is known
that the structure of the atom was very much in his thinking. To Professor W. H. Bragg, who had gone from Cambridge to Adelaide, Australia, and who was now at Leeds
in England, he wrote in 1911:

> Did I tell you that Hahn finds that the penetrating beta
> rays from a simple product are not homogeneous . . .? I
> think I can offer an explanation of that . . . I can see
> that the working out of a complete theory of the alpha and
> beta rays is going to be rather a large job; but the outlook
> is very promising. . . .

What was the inside of the atom like? Rutherford was not
the first of brilliant physicists to ask the question. In fact,
there were several answers which took the form of 'models.'
The physicist's model is nothing you can touch, see or feel.
It is a picture of an idea, but the idea must be tested by
experiment. The German physicist, Philipp Lenard, at the
University of Heidelberg, thought the atom was made up of
'dynamids' — a name he gave to an electron and a positive

---

* It was at this Congress in 1910, that it was agreed that the amount of
radium emanation in equilibrium with one gram of radium should be
called a 'Curie.'

charge, pairs of which were supposed to be scattered through a large space in the atom. How did he arrive at this idea? He found that while a very small part of the atom stopped swift cathode rays, the major part of it permitted them to get through as if through empty space.

On the other hand, J. J. Thompson conceived the atom to be a sphere of positive electrification, in which the electrons, arranged in rings, were imbedded. On the matter of the atom's structure, teacher and pupil disagreed. The pupil expressed his idea in a famous paper, 'The Scattering of Alpha and Beta Particles of Matter and the Structure of the Atom.' In it, Rutherford described the results of a series of experiments on the bombardment of gold foil with beams of alpha particles. When a stream of alpha particles was fired at a thin sheet of foil, most of the particles passed through. So far, the observation was the same as others had noted. What was different?

Some of the particles, he found, were turned aside slightly, emerging from the gold foil at a small angle from their original path. But a few were deflected by large angles; what's more, an occasional particle actually came back, emerging from the same side of the foil it went in!

The genius of Rutherford is shown by the fact that this phenomenon gave him pause. Where others might have regarded these occasional bounce backs as minor accidents of the experiment, Rutherford wrote: 'It was quite the most incredible event that ever happened to me in my life. It was almost as incredible as if you had fired a 15-inch shell at a piece of tissue paper and it came back and hit you.' These deflections which he observed were much larger than could possibly be accounted for by either the Lenard or Thomson model. And so Rutherford proposed his own.

He pictured the atom as composed of a central charge (only later was this to be called the nucleus) surrounded by a sphere of electrification of equal but opposite charge. At this time, too, he wasn't sure whether the charge was positive or negative. 'For convenience,' he said, 'the sign will be assumed positive.' From his measurements of the particles that bounced back from the foil, or were deflected through a large angle, he calculated the probable size of the central core, and the diameter of the surrounding space. He found that the number of particles turned back by the foil was proportional to the atomic weight of the material and the thickness of the foil. He assumed that the size of the atom's central charge was proportional to its atomic weight. And so his model was indeed a simple one: a central core of electric charge, which we now call the nucleus, surrounded by a sphere of electrification which he later discovered was negative.

The nucleus of hydrogen has a charge of 1, the nucleus of helium 2, of lithium 3, and of plutonium 94. We call these the *atomic numbers* – the number of unit positive charges on the atomic nuclei of an element. A student of Heidelberg (at that time) writing today says: 'The paper produced no kind of sensation in the world of physics.' Apparently, Rutherford himself, though sure of his results, did not realize at the time, 'the supreme importance they were to have.' Two years later, writing about the structure of the nucleus, he said: 'No doubt the positively charged center of the atom is a complicated system in movement, consisting in part of charged helium and hydrogen atoms,' and further: 'It would appear as if the positively charged atoms of matter attract one another at very small distances, for otherwise it is difficult to see how the component parts at the center are held together.' Forty years later, it is still not clear what force holds these charges together.

While the world did not at first recognize the full significance of Rutherford's greatest discovery, one man who came to Manchester from Copenhagen, Denmark immediately saw the prospects of further discovery which were opened up as a result of the new atomic model. This man was Niels Bohr. There were some 'kinks' which needed 'ironing out.'

While working in Rutherford's laboratory for several months he published a paper in 1912, in which he established the structure of the atom — a nucleus surrounded by electrons. Niels Bohr, whom we will meet again, carried on from there.

Rutherford's own comments years after he made the discovery reflect his underestimation of it at the time. To Geiger he wrote: 'They were happy days in Manchester, and we wrought better than we knew.'

World War I interrupted much of the work in England. Some of the younger men left their laboratories to take up technical projects connected with the pursuit of the war, while others went off to the battlefields. Among them was H. G. J. Moseley, a young physicist who, in 1915, finally clinched the orderly arrangement of nuclear charge, by which the atomic number increases by regular steps as we go from one element to the next. Moseley, at the age of twenty-seven, was killed in the battle of Gallipoli. Rutherford himself joined the Admiralty Board of Invention and Research, working on the problem of submarine detection. When he returned to his laboratory in 1917, he was working with but one assistant in an empty laboratory, counting scintillations produced when atoms in air were knocked out and hit the zinc sulfide screen.

In 1918, when J. J. was appointed Master of Trinity College, Rutherford was offered the Cavendish Professorship. The pupil of 1895 became the logical successor to his great teacher, and he moved to Cambridge. Again, the work on radioactivity was resumed with new workers from England, the United States, and the Soviet Union, the last being represented by P. L. Kapitza. Discoveries leading to the penetration of the nucleus, its components, the proton and later the neutron, followed.

In addition to directing research Rutherford was called on to perform other duties. Between 1925 and 1930 he was

President of the Royal Society, again succeeding his teacher. Then he became Chairman of the Advisory Council of the Department of Scientific and Industrial Research. In addition he gave innumerable lectures and addresses to societies in different parts of the world.

In 1931 his government honored him once more. He was created a Baron. From then on he was Lord Rutherford or Baron Rutherford of Nelson, linking his name with the town near where he was born, and where he went to school. The cable he immediately sent to his mother read: 'Now Lord Rutherford, more your honour than mine, Ernest.'

He was invited to deliver the Presidential Address to the Indian Science Congress which was to be held in January 1938, but he was never to make the journey. In the fall of 1937, he underwent a minor operation from which he didn't recover. He died within five days.

On October 19, 1937, at the age of sixty-six, young in spirit, and in the midst of his active and glorious life, Lord Rutherford joined the immortals of science. The epoch which he ushered in was by no means at an end. The full fruits of his work had not yet been realized, and the men he taught and with whom he worked continued to reveal the mysteries of the tiny cosmos, and later to split it apart.

ALBERT EINSTEIN
(1879–1955)

Formula for Atom's Energy

WE TEMPORARILY LEAVE the Cavendish Laboratory to continue our story at a government office in Bern, Switzerland. It is 1905, and the place is a patent office, where a German-born physicist-mathematician is examining applications for patents on reported inventions. His name is Albert Einstein. He would much rather be teaching in a University, work for which he is fitted by training, ability, and interest, but a teaching post has not been available to him. Even though he has adopted Switzerland as his country, he is what the Swiss-born patriots call only a 'paper Swiss.' Besides, his Jewish ancestry adds to his difficulty in obtaining a teaching or research post.

His work in the patent office for the last five years, though of a routine sort, has not dulled his sharp mind. In fact his occupation with inventions has given him a kind of satisfying exercise in getting at the kernel of the idea that was the basis for each invention. Besides, it has left him a good deal of leisure to study the work of other physicists and philosophers. More than that, during this time he has formulated his own ideas on questions of matter and energy. Some scientists, like Rutherford and Thomson, arrived at their theories through their laboratory experiments, but Einstein was a scientist of another sort – a theoretical physicist. His apparatus was simple and homely indeed – a pencil and paper, or blackboard and chalk.

In 1903, Rutherford and Soddy, after investigating the energies of alpha particles, wrote, 'All these considerations point to the conclusion that the energy latent in the atom must be enormous. . . .' But just how much energy is bound up in the atom? Thanks to Einstein the answer could now be obtained from a formula. In his paper on the Theory of Relativity (1905), he made the bold suggestion that matter and energy, previously thought to be separate and distinct, could be changed one into the other.

Long before protons, neutrons, or positrons, had been heard of, Einstein showed that in processes in which particles are moving at very high speed, (and this is true in the interior of disintegrating atoms, the process discovered by the Curies and Rutherford) the *mass which disappears becomes energy.*

To describe this idea, which makes it possible to calculate just how much energy is given off, the mathematician-physicist wrote the formula:

$$E = mc^2$$

which means:

Energy produced = mass lost X the square of the speed of light

E   stands for Energy, expressed in ergs (energy units)

m   stands for mass or weight in grams

c   stands for the speed of light – 186,000 miles per second.

Using this formula, it can be calculated that a gram (1/28 of an ounce) of any substance would yield a quantity of energy sufficient to lift ten million tons one kilometer (.62 mile) high, a distance four times the height of the Woolworth building.

Actually only about one-thousandth of the energy is realized. If that is so, then 1 pound of any substance would yield as much power as 3 million pounds or 1,500 tons of coal. Still a tremendous force!

What do we know about the man who at the age of twenty-six wrote the formula by which we can calculate the amount of energy produced in the splitting of an atom of matter?

IN 1879, in the small Bavarian city of Ulm, Albert Einstein was born on March 14. But he was only a year old when his family moved to Munich, a much larger city. In Munich, the Einsteins lived in a suburban house surrounded by a garden. Albert's father, Hermann Einstein, operated a small electrochemical factory, of which he was the technical director, while his brother attended to the business end of the establishment. The business didn't go very well, even with his brother's help, because Hermann was not especially good at business. He enjoyed his life away from the factory, and took the family on outings to the beautiful lake and mountain country surrounding Munich. He liked the good beer served with radishes and sausages in the Bavarian taverns.

Schiller and Heine, Germany's famous poets, were Hermann Einstein's favorites; he had only a mild interest in politics, and no interest at all in the orthodox Jewish customs of keeping the Sabbath or the dietary laws. His brother, who lived with the family, was interested in the intellectual life of his time. Trained as an engineer, he was largely responsible for his nephew's early interest in mathematics.

From his mother, Albert learned to love German classical music. He remembered evenings when engineers from his father's factory dropped in for a visit and his mother played Beethoven's sonatas on the piano with one of the visitors. During the day, Albert's mother was kept busy with house-

12. *Dr. Albert Einstein in his study in Princeton, N.J.*

13. *Dr. F. W. Aston.*

hold chores and with the care of the children – Albert and his younger sister.

When he was small, Albert worried his parents. They were afraid he would not grow up to be a normal child because he was a long time in learning to speak, he sat by himself, daydreaming, and didn't take part in children's games. He considered himself too weak for physical play, especially for playing at being a soldier. Other children imitated the marching soldiers, who were a common sight in the streets of Munich in militarized Germany under Bismarck. He would say to his parents about such parades: 'When I grow up I don't want to be one of those poor people.' He considered soldiers unfortunate because he thought they were forced to behave like automatons. His lifelong hatred of militarism and of any form of coercion may have had its beginnings in these childhood impressions.

The schools of Einstein's days were denominational. Since the Jewish school was far from their home, and his parents were not especially interested in a Jewish education for Albert, they sent him to a Catholic elementary school, where he was the only Jew in his class. He received instruction in the Catholic religion, and derived a great deal of pleasure from it, learning his lessons so well that he could help the Catholic children with their lessons in religion. Except for the religious lessons, he didn't like school, because he imagined life in the barracks to be much like the disciplined life of the classroom. He balked at learning the answers to questions mechanically, and hated the necessity of standing at attention when spoken to by the teacher.

At the age of nine, when he still lacked fluency of speech, deliberating slowly before expressing himself, his mother tried to overcome her fear that he might turn out to be odd, by saying: 'Maybe he will become a great professor some day.'

When Albert was ten, he entered the gymnasium, where much of the time was devoted to learning Latin and Greek grammar. Young Einstein didn't find it any more to his liking than the elementary school. He wanted to know what the world was about. He was not interested in memorizing the laws of grammar, and the Prussian discipline was extremely distasteful. He often said: 'The teachers in the elementary school appeared to me like sergeants, and the gymnasium teachers like lieutenants.' Only one among his teachers, a man named Ruess, tried to bring to his pupils the spirit of the ancient cultures; of his lessons, Albert couldn't get enough.

As Albert grew up and began to choose his own books, he read a great many popular ones on natural science which were available at the time. From these he learned about plants and animals, their interdependence and the theories of their origins. He was even more interested in the stars, meteors, earthquakes, volcanoes, geology, and climate. Later he went on to such books as Büchner's *Force and Matter* and began to get some idea of the organization of the universe. He also got hold of a geometry textbook before the work was taken up in his class, becoming absorbed in it.

The steps in the proof of a proposition seemed so clear and reasoned that these also impressed him with the orderliness of the mathematical world, as contrasted with what he thought was disorderly outside it.

By the time he was thirteen, he had learned to play the violin well enough to get deep pleasure from Mozart's sonatas, and for the first time he gained real pleasure from playing for many hours. Soon his skill improved sufficiently so that he could take part in a chamber music performance.

In the gymnasium he received instruction in the Jewish religion. While he was stirred by the Proverbs of Solomon and the parts of the Old Testament that dealt with ethics – questions of right and wrong – he acquired a distaste for the rituals of orthodox religion. He made up his mind that after graduation he would not become a member of any organized religion or church.

WHEN ALBERT was fifteen and not yet out of the gymnasium, his father's business failed, and the family decided to seek its fortune in what his father thought was a happier country. They left for Milan, Italy, but Albert was to stay in Munich for another year to complete his gymnasium course. The diploma was necessary for entrance into a University; besides, the least that any middle-class German was expected to achieve was a gymnasium diploma. The boy was most unhappy both in his boarding-house home and in school, where he excelled only in mathematics. He found his other classroom studies dull, and resented his classmates who tried to get him to take part in athletics. How could he get away from this miserable place where he felt like a stranger? He had a plan: he would ask a doctor to give him a letter saying he had a nervous breakdown and needed to spend six months with his parents in Italy. But this turned out to be unnecessary, because one day his teacher told him that he had better leave school. What had he done now, he wondered? The teacher told him that his indifference to his studies destroyed the respect of other students for the teachers.

And so he was off to Milan. The first thing he told his father was that he wanted to give up his German citizenship. Since his father remained a German, this complicated matters. Because it would take some time before he could acquire citizenship on his own, he was temporarily 'a man without a country.' This was also the time when he renounced his legal attachment to the Jewish community.

Life in Italy was a real joy. He wandered through the churches and art museums, becoming ecstatic over the works of art. It seemed to him that there was music everywhere — in the streets, and in the melodious voices of the people. He hiked through the Apennine Mountains. Most of all he was impressed with the ease and naturalness of the people, an atmosphere so wonderfully different from that of the Germany he knew. But the release from the disciplined automaton-like life of his home country was short-lived.

His father was no more successful in Italy than he had been in Germany. One day he announced to Albert that he could no longer support him. He would have to look about for some professional training so that he could earn his own living. But how? He had left the gymnasium without a diploma. Was his interest in the pure sciences of physics and mathematics enough to admit him to a technical school? Perhaps.

He went to a famous technical school in Zurich, Switzerland, and took the entrance examination. But he failed, because while his training in mathematics was ahead of that of other applicants, his preparation fell short in botany, zoology, and languages. The director of the Polytechnic School, recognizing his unusual ability in mathematics, advised him to obtain a Swiss diploma. Did this mean going back to a regimented institution of the kind he was familiar with? He wasn't happy at the prospect.

To his great surprise the cantonal school in Arau was very different. No militaristic drill; the teachers were human and friendly; there were student laboratories with apparatus where one could experiment; there was a museum and microscopes for studying living things; there were maps and pictures for geography. It was here that Albert lost his dislike of school, and even became friendly, socializing with his fellow students. He lived in the home of one of his teachers, enjoying the companionship of his son and daughter; together they took trips to the mountains. After one year he obtained his diploma and was admitted to the Polytechnic School in Zurich.

Strangely enough, in the school where he was supposed to learn a practical profession, he soon decided that what he really wanted was to teach physics and mathematics in an advanced school. He entered the department that trained teachers in these two subjects. This was the time when theoretical physics had reached a turning point, and Einstein became immersed in the stimulating work which was being published in Germany. The Polytechnic School also attracted many serious students from eastern and southeastern Europe where, for political reasons, they could not or would not study. Einstein found a common bond with these young people who were so earnest and purposeful.

Among his acquaintances was a young woman from Hungary. Like Einstein, Mileva Maritsch had a passion for the study of physics, and they spent a great deal of time together, he thinking out loud, she not always listening. He was so immersed in his own words that he often didn't notice her unresponsiveness.

In 1900, Einstein completed his studies and looked around for a position. The modest sum he had been receiving from a wealthy relative during his training period, out of which he saved enough to become a Swiss citizen, was now to be cut off. What he wanted and needed to prepare him for work as scientific investigator was an assistantship in a university. Despite the praise he received from his teachers, no such job was offered him at the Polytechnic. Nor could he obtain a position at a secondary school. A temporary job in a vocational school was also to end after a few months. The next tutoring work in a gymnasium turned out to be no more lasting; besides this type of teaching wasn't to his taste, and so Einstein was again unemployed.

It was then that a friend introduced him to the Director of the patent office in Bern. He now received a steady salary of 3,000 francs a year, a sum on which he could live comfortably, enough even to marry. Soon afterwards he married the reserved and stern Mileva, whose stolid personality often clashed with his open and enthusiastic nature. When two sons were born to them, Einstein was very happy with them, deriving a great deal of pleasure in watching them grow up.

Einstein was one of those geniuses of whom it is said that only one is born in a century, and whose conviction is as great as their thinking is revolutionary. When he brought forth his theory of the relativity of time and space, few men understood his ideas, and many more didn't believe them. Even so, there were those who sensed the importance of his results, published in 1905, describing new laws of motion requiring hitherto unknown ways of measuring them. Somehow the incongruity of his position as a petty official and the immensity of his discovery became apparent to the physicists of the Swiss universities. Could he now teach at the University of Zurich, some of them asked?

There was still one stumbling block in his way. The rule of Swiss and other continental universities was that before becoming a professor, one had to serve a kind of apprenticeship in which his ability could be demonstrated. First he had to become a *Privatdozent,* giving free lectures at the university – as many or as few as he liked. There were not many who could afford the luxury of such an arrangement, but Einstein could manage it because he had his job, which gave him both the leisure and a sustaining salary.

Einstein took the advice of friends and accepted the opening as *Privatdozent,* but few students attended his lectures, largely because he didn't make them understandable. So when an opening for a professorship in theoretical physics became available, the board of trustees, unimpressed with him as a teacher, chose someone else, – a former fellow-student at Polytechnic. Friedrich Adler, learning that he was in competition with Einstein, told the board: 'If it is possible to obtain a man like Einstein for our university, it would be absurd to appoint me.'

Despite the objections to Einstein, he was finally appointed, in 1909, as professor 'extraordinary' at the University of Zurich.

For the first time, at the age of thirty, Einstein enjoyed some prestige, but financially his job was no better than the one he had relinquished at the patent office. In fact, to keep up his present social position, his wife had to earn additional money by boarding students. Einstein once remarked: 'In my relativity theory I set up a clock at every point in space, but in reality I find it difficult to provide even one clock in my room.' Besides, there were demands on his time for all kinds of duties which he considered extremely unimportant compared with the creative work he wished to pursue. He had even less use for the formalities that go with such a position and the social obligations towards his colleagues. Einstein saw no reason for talking any differently to the heads of the university than to his cobbler or the scrub-woman who kept the laboratory clean. While simple folk found his humor and friendliness pleasing, his unaffected behavior offended some of his official superiors. Perhaps it was just as well that the next year he was called to teach physics at the German University in Prague (then Austria).

Here, too, difficulties preceded him. He was a foreigner, had a Slavic wife, and was not a member of any official community. On the last point, he compromised and inserted the word 'Mosaic' (as the Jews were called in Austria) in the Blank on the questionnaire next to 'Religion.' His non-conformism – from his long hair to his failure to observe the custom of paying formal calls on his colleagues – again rubbed people the wrong way. Such things gave Einstein little concern; he accepted them as petty stupidities.

There was, however, another circumstance of his relation-ship to faculty and the community which disturbed him. The University of Prague, one of the oldest in Europe, was divided into two completely different schools: German and Czech. Professors lectured in their respective languages, and even those teaching the same subject had no contact with each other. It was not unusual for such professors to meet for the first time at an International Congress in Chicago.

Ninety-five per cent of the people were Czech. The re-maining five per cent – Germans – were even at that time spreading the idea of a 'master race,' and regarded the Czechs as inferiors. Einstein found the jokes and disparag-ing anecdotes about his Czech neighbors offensive. The

Czechs, in turn, as the victims of hostility, were naturally sensitive to these insults and were suspicious of every German. This stood in the way of even a German like Einstein making friends with the Czechs, despite the fact that he showed his disapproval of the hostile attitude of his colleagues. It was indeed rarely that some Czech students attended his classes and carried on research under his direction.

It was in Prague, too, that Einstein, through his awareness of the problems of the Czech people, came to understand also the problems of the Jewish community of which for the first time since his childhood he became a part. The Jewish tradesmen and peasants spoke Czech; they constituted the majority of the people, and kept apart from those Jews who aped the Germans, taking on their language and supporting their cultural activities such as the theatres, concerts, and lectures. To the Czech-speaking people these Jews were identical with the Germans, a hostile foreign power that was driving them into war.

To be sure, it wasn't long before the Nazi creed of Aryan superiority, even long before it took root in Germany, was already showing itself as Sudeten-German hostility toward the Jews. A group of Jews who disliked taking sides between the German and Czech nationalists began to develop their own intellectual life. They were the Zionists who at that time were less interested in politics than in art, literature, music, and philosophy. Einstein was introduced to this group, but Zionism didn't interest him. In fact, the problems of nationality seemed to him petty, and the tensions caused by these nationalistic feelings were, to him, expressions of human stupidity. It wasn't until much later that he came to recognize that these local troubles were to take on world proportions.

While in Prague, Einstein founded his new theory of gravitation. He was also working on the nature of light, and was troubled by the problem of its two-fold character: wave and particle, a seeming contradiction which was not reconciled until some time later. His stay in Prague was short, for soon after he came there he was invited to take a full professorship at the Polytechnic School in Zurich, from which he had graduated. At first he was hesitant about leaving Prague where he had made some friends, but he was persuaded by his wife, who felt more at home in Zurich, and so in the fall of 1912 he took up his duties at Polytechnic.

His return to the school where he had once failed to enter as a student was now hailed as an honor bestowed on the institution. Einstein had by then made a name for himself. At the Radiology Congress in 1910 in Brussels where the leading physicists – Rutherford, Langevin, Max Planck, Madame Curie – had gathered, he took his rightful place among the scientists who were shaping the ideas of modern physics. At that time, Planck the pre-eminent theoretical physicist wrote: 'If Einstein's theory should prove to be correct, as I expect it will, he will be considered the Copernicus of the twentieth century.' As time went on, his reputation grew with each elaboration of his theory.

By 1913, his pre-eminence as a world scientist was unquestioned. A special position was created for him as Director of the new Kaiser-Wilhelm Physical Institute in Berlin. He was given a salary large enough to enable him to devote all his time to research without restrictions or routine duties. The Institute was founded by Kaiser Wilhelm II with funds received from rich industrialists, bankers, and merchants. Germany was competing with the rest of Europe and the United States as an industrial nation, and required trained scientists for her rapid development. The Institute was modeled after the Rockefeller and Carnegie Institutes in the United States and secured for the German Reich leading scientists, who, because of the stifling atmosphere at the universities, might have been excluded from these institutions for political or religious reasons.

It was a difficult decision for Einstein to make. Should he

return to Germany from which he had fled as a student? It seemed to him a betrayal of his convictions to become a member of a social group he disliked. But there were enormous advantages for his further development as a science investigator, and so he followed the advice of his German colleagues and accepted the offer. The move to Berlin was to bring another change in his life. His wife, Mileva, didn't wish to follow him, and since a lack of sympathy had grown up between them by then, making separation easy, Einstein became a bachelor once more.

He was elected a member of the Royal Prussian Academy of Science at the age of thirty-four, still a young man among those who held this much sought honor. This, like many academic distinctions, meant very little to Einstein. Long before this, a colleague had once remarked that it was a pity that no one ever entered the Academy while young, at a time when it could still make him happy. To this Einstein replied: 'If that is the case. I could be elected to the Academy immediately, since it would not make me happy even now.'

Whether Einstein cared or not, honors were showered upon him. He was elected foreign member of the Royal Society, to the Amsterdam and Copenhagen Academies; he received honorary degrees from Geneva, Manchester, and Princeton; the Copley medal from the Royal Society and the gold medal of the Royal Astronomical Society. In 1921 he was awarded the Nobel Prize for his theory of relativity. Referring to this period of twenty years when Einstein was in Berlin, it has often been stated: 'There were two kinds of physicists: on the one hand was Einstein, and on the other all the rest.'

For all his greatness, Einstein was a simple, kindly, and likeable person. He was naturally friendly, ready to talk to anyone about anything, to laugh and joke and tell stories. At the same time he had a certain aloofness where his colleagues in academic circles were concerned. He had no use for the formalities so important in a professorial community. It was not out of a sense of superiority that he seemed to live in a world of his own, managing to surround himself with a 'free space' where he was protected from all disturbances. His material requirements were always of the most modest. At the peak of his world fame, when Professor Arthur Compton visited him in Berlin, he found that 'he was living in a small, rather dingy apartment approached by a narrow flight of stairs.' The dress that people saw him in most often consisted of slacks and sweater, and when at home he was in his stocking feet, even when receiving visitors.

In his relationship with students he was again unlike the usual professor. He disliked giving lectures in a regular course of physics, preferring to converse informally with students concerning their research programs. He was remarkably patient in answering their questions, and equally interested in original ideas from them. At his first meeting with his class at Prague he said to the students: 'I shall always be able to receive you. If you have a problem, come to me with it. You will never disturb me, since I can interrupt my own work at any moment and resume it immediately as soon as the interruption is past.' For his own part, he could never understand why, when he wished to discuss a problem with a colleague, he was expected to make arrangements in advance, or why he had to engage in small talk before getting to the point that was on his mind.

Before his first year in Berlin was over, in August, 1914, Germany was at war. Einstein was again an outsider. German scientists and intellectuals signed the Manifesto of the Ninenty-Two, declaring that German culture and German militarism are identical. Needless to say, Einstein was not one of them, and only his Swiss citizenship, making him a 'neutral,' saved him from being looked on as a traitor. All of his colleagues became active in some kind of war work — constructing submarine sound detectors, or other projects.

They deprecated the work of scientists in other countries as superficial and 'idealistic.'

Before Einstein came to Berlin he was considered by his German relatives to be the black sheep of the family. He had run away from the Munich gymnasium, had given up his religion and citizenship; his devotion to physics brought him a poor income, and, on top of that, he had married a woman of the Greek Orthodox faith. But now that he was world famous, they were not only astonished, but felt honored at being known as his relatives. Einstein was amused at this and accepted it good-naturedly. In fact, it was pleasant to be invited to his uncle's house for a home-cooked meal, a welcome change from the restaurant fare which was prepared according to the instructions of the German military authorities. Here he renewed his child-hood friendship with his cousin Elsa, who was now a widow with two daughters.

Her friendliness – even motherliness – helped to create a warm home atmosphere where Einstein found a new family life. Frau Elsa had none of the intellectual abilities of Mileva Maritsch, but her happy disposition more than made up for her inability to discuss physics. How different she was from the austere, hard, and cold Mileva. Elsa was immensely proud of her famous cousin, and she tried in every way to make his life as pleasant as she could. She once told a friend of Einstein's: 'I know very well what a talented physicist our Albertle is . In these times we have to buy food in all kinds of cans which no one knows how to open. Often they are of unfamiliar, foreign make, rusted, bent, and without the key necessary to open them. But there hasn't been a single one yet that our Albertle has not been able to open.'

Before long Einstein married Elsa, and settled down to a middle-class way of life in a spacious apartment in a fashionable part of Berlin. Frau Einstein knew how to maintain a household suitable to her station in life, and to entertain in a style to which Einstein was unaccustomed. Einstein had always been indifferent to regular mealtimes, but now his meals were served regularly and guests were received in a beautifully furnished home.

This change didn't change his outlook on life, however, any more than the esteem in which he was held influenced him in the company he chose to keep. His professional colleagues looked down their noses where Elsa was concerned. They didn't regard her as a wife suited to a great man. Their criticism of Elsa may have been a sign of jealousy because Einstein preferred to mingle with all kinds of people, rather than exclusively with professors. In Elsa, Einstein found a loving, admiring, and devoted wife.

Despite the war, which distracted other scientists, Einstein continued with his work, and by 1916 he had developed a completely independent and unified theory of gravitation, which differed fundamentally from that of Newton. For motions of bodies in outer space he found that the rates predicted according to the old laws were not the same as the actual rates. This was true, for instance, in the case of the planet Mercury. Einstein introduced the idea that space has curvature, and that time added a fourth dimension which had to be accounted for in the calculation of the rate of motion. But all this was in the realm of mathematics. The new conception of gravitation still had to be proved by the measurements of the astronomer. An opportunity to do just that would come on March 29, 1919 when there was to be a total solar eclipse.

The Royal Astronomical Society of London appointed a committee to make preparations for an expedition. One observation post was set up in northern Brazil and the other on the isle of Principe in the Gulf of Guinea, West Africa. Despite the unfavorable weather, which clouded the photographs, some were properly exposed. When the photographs of stars taken in London were compared with those obtained of the same ones on the expedition, the shift in the position was in accordance with Einstein's calculations. The results were reported before the Royal Society on November 6, 1919. On the next day, along with headlines announcing the first anniversary of the signing of the Armistice, the London *Times* carried another: REVOLUTION IN SCIENCE. NEWTONIAN IDEAS OVERTHROWN. Opening the session of the Royal Society, J. J. Thomson hailed Einstein's theory as 'one of the greatest achievements in the history of human thought.'

In Germany the news was received with double satisfaction. Einstein was at this time 'one of their own.' A German scientist, son of a defeated and humiliated country, had been honored by the proudest of the victorious nations. However, this happy circumstance was soon to be forgotten. Einstein had become a public figure; scientists were not the only ones to recognize his achievement now. While Einstein was never interested in active politics, he was not afraid to risk his great reputation for any cause he believed in.

In defeated Germany, the supporters of the overthrown rulers spread the idea that the defeat was due to the internal revolt led by Jews. The spread of anti-Semitism caused Einstein to join the Zionist forces. While he was never in sympathy with strong nationalistic sentiments, he looked upon the Jews, because of their regard for intellectual values, as the bearers of a great tradition. For the Jewish community, Einstein became a symbol of a creative intellectual power, in direct refutation of the Nordic-Aryan myth that the Jews (among others) were 'inferior.' Einstein was also a pacifist, having hated militarism from the time he was a child. In 1922 he was appointed to the 'Commission pour la Cooperation Intellectuelle' of the League of Nations. But a year later, when he saw that the League of Nations failed to prevent the use of force by great nations he resigned.

For the ardent German nationalists, the Jews and the pacifists became the scapegoats, and Einstein was beginning to feel the pressures of 'racial' hostility. Not the least of those who became his enemies were the German intellectuals. When he was asked whether he would be willing to leave Berlin, he said: 'Would such a decision be so amazing? My situation is like that of a man who is lying in a beautiful bed where he is being tortured by bedbugs.' However, he didn't act on it immediately, and even became a German citizen.

The attacks against him only aroused the interest of people over the world, and he was invited by many countries to lecture on his theory. He traveled everywhere – Europe, Asia, and America. Wherever he lectured, at universities and at overcrowded meetings, thousands gathered to hear the world-famous man who had overthrown the old laws explaining the universe. Especially in the United States did he receive the kind of enthusiastic demonstration accorded the most distinguished who visit its shores. The reporters and cameramen turned out at the pier, bombarding him with questions and flash bulbs, so that Einstein said he felt like a 'prima donna.' The light vein in which he explained the amazing interest in his theory was that the ladies in New York want to have a new style each year. 'This year the fashion is relativity,' he jokingly remarked.

Actually, of course, the eagerness with which people listened to him expressed their genuine desire to understand his work and to pay homage to a great scientist. Those who understood his theory had even more reason to honor him. When he was presenting Einstein with an honorary degree, the President of Princetown University said: 'We salute the new Columbus of science voyaging through strange seas of thought alone.' Despite the hostility in certain quarters towards Einstein because, by accident of birth, he was a German and a Jew, to most people throughout the world he was a messenger of international good will and understanding.

He returned to Berlin in 1924, and except for a trip to South America the next year, and to Pasadena, California in 1930, he remained at his post in the Institute until the fall of 1932. Early the next year, when Hitler became Chancellor, a racial purge took place in the universities. Einstein was still in California when the purge began. In a conversation with the German consul's deputy in which Einstein made known his decision not to return to Germany, he was told: 'Herr Professor, now that we are speaking man to man, I can only tell you that you are doing the right thing.'

In May 1933, a physicist, who had long been an enemy of Einstein, stated in a published article: 'The most important example of the dangerous influence of Jewish circles on the study of nature has been provided by Herr Einstein with his mathematically botched-up theories consisting of some ancient knowledge and a few arbitary additions. . . .'

Einstein went to Belgium and from there conducted a correspondence with the Prussian Academy which resulted in their cowardly acceptance of his resignation. The Bavarian Academy expelled him from its ranks. His country home was searched by the political police, and all his possessions and his bank account were confiscated by the state. (Had he not become a citizen of Germany, and remained a Swiss, his personal property would have been saved from confiscation.) His writings, together with the books of others, were burned publicly in the square before the State Opera House in Berlin.

But even before this happened the way had been paved for Einstein's emigration to the United States. In Princeton, New Jersey, a wholly novel institution had been founded in 1930. With a fund of five million dollars donated by Mrs. Felix Fuld, and Mr. Louis Bamberger, a department store owner, The Institute for Advanced Study was established on the advice of Dr. Abraham Flexner who was its first director. The Institute has no connection with Princeton University; in fact, it is unlike the ordinary university. It does not offer courses, grant degrees, or conduct laboratory research. It is open to a small group of outstanding scientists and scholars who come from all over the

14. *Professor Frederick Soddy.*

15. *Sir James Chadwick.*

world to this scholarly retreat where they carry on their work without having to give a thought to teaching schedules or administrative duties.

Dr. Flexner personally extended the invitation to Albert Einstein to become a a life member of the Institute. In 1933 he took up his work here, where he had left off in Berlin. There were details of establishing a residency of five years, after which Einstein became a citizen of the United States.

He was proud to become an American. 'Here is the last refuge of freedom. It is only the United States that can save the world,' he said. In the words of Arthur Compton: 'Einstein made free use of his extraordinary scientific reputation as a platform for promoting his humanitarian interests. Central among these was the establishment of a peaceful world in which men and women might live in freedom. He did all in his power to bring such a world into being.'

The man who gave the world the formula for unlocking the atom's storehouse of energy played one more significant part in its release – but this is to come later in our story.

LINKS IN THE ATOM CHAIN

We must now return to England where the work of four Nobel Prize Winners, pupils and co-workers of Thomson and Rutherford forged the next links in the chain of discoveries that made possible the release of atomic energy.

C. T. R. WILSON
(1869–   )

ONE OF THOMSON'S celebrated pupils was C. T. R. Wilson who invented the *cloud chamber*. The idea came from J. J., who one day remarked to Wilson that he needed an instrument to photograph the tracks of individual electrons moving through a gas. The strange thing is that Wilson didn't think that the great master had suddenly gone stark mad. With all seriousness he went ahead with the construction of the needed instrument.

Charles Thomson Rees Wilson, a farmer's son, was born in Glencoers, Scotland in February, 1869. He studied botany, geology, and zoology at Manchester, and in 1888 he went to Cambridge as a research student on the scholarship system. While still in Scotland he studied cloud phenomena from the Observatory on top of Ben Nevis, the highest mountain in Scotland. In 1900 he published a paper on his observation that a few ions are always being produced in air. It was at this time that he was appointed instructor and demonstrator in meteorological physics at Cambridge. Continuing his research into atmospheric electricity, especially radioactivity of rain and snow, he measured the electricity of the atmosphere. Wilson possessed great manipulative skill; it is said that no one has ever performed more beautiful experiments by means of ingenious instruments, which he himself devised. No wonder that J. J. picked him; the man knew clouds and could contrive all sorts of devices!

The cloud chamber was a box with windows and a movable piston in its bottom. Air saturated with water vapor was led into the box through a window on one side. As the piston was moved down, the air in the box expanded and cooled, so that part of the vapor condensed into a light fog or cloud. Just as water vapor in the clouds in the sky condenses into liquid best when it is around dust particles or electrically charged air molecules, so also in the box. Wilson permitted a stream of electrons from an outside source to pass through another opening in the box. As droplets of moisture collected around the ions, they spread out, forming a strip wide enough to be seen with the naked eye. This wide streak in the thinner fog around it could then be photographed. In this way a picture was made of the paths of electrons which moved through the box.

Not only electrons, but any moving particles that ionize gases, leave fog tracks in the cloud chamber. In this way Wilson made it possible to see particles that were too small to be photographed directly. Not only the paths, but collisions of high-speed particles as they take a sudden switch in their paths could thus be photographed. The cloud chamber became a useful instrument first for J. J. and later for Rutherford's study of alpha particles. The tracks of the positron and the meson particles discovered later were also photographed from their path in the cloud chamber. Thus the cloud chamber was an important tool for studying atomic particles and their behavior.

Wilson continued lecturing on atmospheric electricity and, in 1895, became Jackson Professor of Physics at Cambridge. He received prizes and medals from the Cambridge Philosophical Society, from the Edinburgh Royal Society and from The Franklin Institute. In 1927, jointly with Arthur Compton, he received the Nobel Prize in physics, for 'discovery of his method of rendering discernible the courses of electrically charged particles by water condensation.'

F. W. ASTON

(1877–1945)

ANOTHER OF J. J.'s pupils was F. W. Aston, born at Harbourne, near Birmingham, England on September 1, 1877. At the University of Birmingham he studied the chemistry of fermentation, and later turned to experiments in physics, working on the electrical discharge in gases. When a laboratory was established in Birmingham he was appointed Professor Extraordinary. Shortly afterwards he was invited to join the group at Cavendish. During World War I he served as technical head of a Royal Aircraft factory. In 1919 he returned to the Cavendish Laboratory and, with J. J. performed the first experiments on isotopes.

Aston improved on the tube used by Thomson to separate the neon isotopes. He sent positively charged atoms at high speeds through an electric field. In the paths of the escaping ions he placed a large magnet. The heavy atoms were deflected somewhat less than the light atoms. Thus as the beam passed the poles of a magnet, the particles of different mass were separated, and a series of spots formed on a photographic plate. The amount of deflection shown on the photograph provided a very accurate means of determining just how heavy different atoms were. Also from the degree of blackening of the spot (depending upon the number of ions that hit the plate), Aston could gauge the relative amount of each isotope present in any element. In this way Aston found that almost all the elements had isotopes.

Most elements are mixtures of isotopes. The fractions in their atomic weights depend on the relative proportions in which the isotopes are found in nature. The atomic weight of hydrogen is 1.00778. If hydrogen had only one proton and one electron, its atomic weight should have been one. The difference could only be accounted for by the existence of a heavy isotope. But Aston's instrument – the mass spectrometer – showed only one spot. It must be that the heavier isotope was present in such a small amount that it could not be detected on the photographic plate. The work of separating it fell to an American scientist some years later.

But Aston's experiments revised the old idea that all atoms of an element are alike, and that an element is not decomposable. Today, we define an element as a substance whose atoms all have the *same atomic number,* but *not* necessarily the same *atomic weight.* In 1922, the Nobel Prize for Chemistry was awarded to Aston 'for his discovery of the conduct of isotope mixtures in many non-radioactive basic materials and his discovery of the so-called law of complete numbers.' This idea is fundamental to the process of the release of atomic energy, as we shall see later.

FREDERICK SODDY
(1877–1956)

FREDERICK SODDY, Rutherford's young co-worker at McGill University, is perhaps best known for his share in expounding the disintegration theory of radioactivity. In their joint effort to bring light on the subject of spontaneous change of one element into another he is given equal credit with the older and more experienced man. But for various reasons he didn't achieve the status of a Rutherford.

Soddy was born on the southern coast of England, in Eastbourne, in 1877. He was the youngest of seven sons of a London businessman. He was two years old when his mother died, and so, in a household of older brothers, housekeepers, and maids he received little affection and much stern upbringing. Whether for this reason or some other, Soddy kept to himself, making few friends during most of his life, and viewing life's problems with great seriousness. He attended an English public school which is like one of our exclusive private boys' schools. From there he went to Oxford to study chemistry, and graduated in 1898 with high honors.

Soon afterward he took up the post at McGill, later joining Rutherford. In 1903 he returned to London to work with Sir William Ramsay at University College.

Some twenty years later, on the occasion of receiving the Franklin medal, Rutherford wrote: 'I remember well a visit I made to Soddy at University College on the day when Ramsay and he were to collect the emanation from about twenty milligrams of radium to test whether they could detect its spectrum. Soddy told me he would take this opportunity of noting whether any helium was released from radium. That afternoon, the presence of helium was detected by its spectrum. I loaned them my radium to confirm the important discovery.' In this way Soddy showed that

Rutherford's alpha particle was an atom of ionized helium.

During the next ten years Soddy lectured at Glasgow, and then became professor at Aberdeen. In 1908 he married Winifred Beilby, the daughter of a rich industrialist who, with her charm and graciousness, tempered much of his sternness and lack of sociability.

Soddy had made a prediction concerning the end-products of radioactive substances. When radium spontaneously breaks down, its final product is lead. When thorium similarly disintegrates, it also forms lead. Both of these look like ordinary lead, from which they cannot be separated. What were Soddy's predictions concerning these three forms of lead? Were they isotopes, the same element with different atomic weights?

By 1913, some forty or more different radioactive substances were known. Soddy was able to demonstrate that by their chemical properties they could be classified into only about ten substances; the rest should be dubbed isotopes, just like the three kinds of lead.

He received the 1921 Nobel Prize for chemistry, and to his colleague of twenty years earlier, he wrote in gratitude: '. . . acknowledging the debt I owe you for the initiation into the subject of radioactivity in the Montreal days. But for that, I suppose the chance of my ever getting the Nobel Prize would have been exceedingly remote. . . . The paper just arrived and I was delighted to see that Aston gets this year's [1922] Chemistry Prize.'

When World War I was over, in 1919, Soddy, like many others, returned to his scientific work, becoming professor of inorganic and physical chemistry at Oxford. But his heart didn't seem to be in the laboratory. He was deeply impressed with the waste and destruction as well as the futility of the war, and firmly believed that scientists ought to become more interested in social problems, using their knowledge to eradicate the poverty and misery which stalked all of post-war Europe.

The banks and the monetary policy of England, he believed, hindered the bringing of good things to all the people. He favored various schemes to correct these evils, and wrote several books on economics. By this he brought on himself the derision of the economists, and shrugging of the shoulders by scientists, who knew him as an interpreter of atomic structure and spontaneous charge, and a Nobel Prize winner in his chosen field. But though his solutions were not realistic answers to a troubled world's ills, his devotion to peace, expressed in the pacifist writing of his later years, came from a troubled spirit and a generous heart.

When his wife died in 1936, he was broken-hearted and resigned from his professorship at Oxford, retiring at the age of 59. He lived alone at Brighton, England, near where he was born, and died in September 1956.

JAMES CHADWICK
(1891–   )

RUTHERFORD HAD established the existence of the nucleus. The next step was to understand its structure. From a photograph of alpha tracks through nitrogen, he picked out a thinner fog track shooting off in a different direction. In the collision with a nitrogen atom, another particle seemed to have been split off. It had a weaker charge than the alpha particle (about one-fourth) and was equal but opposite in charge of an electron. This positively charged particle was called *proton,* which, in Greek, means 'the first one,' or 'the most important.'

But it soon became clear that nuclei cannot be built up entirely of protons, because their charged particles didn't account for all their weight. For instance, the helium nucleus (alpha particle) had *twice* the electric charge of a proton, but *four* times its weight. It seemed to contain another particle without charge, which acted like so much 'ballast,' weighing as much as the protons.

This particle eluded a number of investigators working in several countries until Chadwick, in Rutherford's laboratory, discovered it in 1932.

James Chadwick was born in Manchester on October 20, 1891. He studied physics at the University of Manchester. In 1912, we learn from Rutherford's letter to Hahn that he and Chadwick were working on the problem of whether gamma rays are produced from alpha rays. Some seven years later they published a book on radiations. But in the meantime, Chadwick had gone to Berlin to work with Hans Geiger at Charlottenburg Institute, little realizing that he would be on an enforced stay there for the duration of the war.

At Ruhleben, where Chadwick was interned for the war period, he, along with other German prisoners, fixed up a little laboratory, in which they conducted experiments on radioactivity. 'I was in the middle of the experiments on beta rays when the war broke out,' he wrote to Rutherford.

After the war, when Chadwick returned to England, he became a Fellow in Cambridge and, in 1923, Assistant Director of Radioactive Research at Cavendish. Together with Rutherford, he had proved that the nuclei of all elements ranging up to potassium — except lithium, carbon, and oxygen — could be disintegrated by the alpha particles of radium C which have energies equivalent to seven million volts. In all cases there was a great repulsive force resisting the close approach of an alpha particle or proton to the nucleus, as if a barrier kept the nucleus intact from intrusion by a 'foreigner.' In the same year Chadwick wrote to Rutherford: 'I think we shall have to make a real search for the neutron. I believe I have a scheme which may just work but I must consult Aston first.' It was to be quite a while before his scheme was to bear fruit.

BOTH IN Germany and in France, experimenters sent streams of alpha particles at beryllium, a light metal. From the bombardment came a beam of rays with very high penetrating power. Some of this radiation penetrated a lead shield that normally absorbs gamma rays. If a paraffin shield or any other hydrogen-containing compound were placed around the beryllium, the rays that entered the paraffin caused the knocking out of particles of very high energy. But what did this all mean?

Chadwick repeated the experiments, getting the same results. He further showed that these rays, like gamma rays and X-rays, could not be deflected by a magnet. This proved that they were neutral. What made them different, however, was their speed, which was only about 1/10 that of light, a speed too slow for gamma rays that travel with almost the speed of light.

As he continued working with these rays, he found that when they were directed against nitrogen, an occasional one would strike the nitrogen atom with terrific force, something gamma rays could not do, for they always bounced off. Since these rays were not deflected by a magnet, he concluded that they were neutral. Since they were absorbed, he decided that they must be particles. Before long he showed that these particles had a mass of 1, the same as a proton, but without its charge. This new particle was the neutron! For his discovery, Chadwick received the Nobel Prize in Physics in 1935.

The discovery of the neutron not only settled the problem of the extra mass in the nucleus, but, as we shall see later, brought the release of the energy from the atom one step nearer. Atomic research took another great surge forward, as the spirit of enthusiasm and excitement over this discovery pervaded the Cavendish and other laboratories.

It became clear that these neutrons, which have remarkable powers of penetrating matter, were themselves extremely efficient agents for the transformation of atoms.

DURING World War II Sir James Chadwick was at work in his own country on uranium separation for the atomic bomb. When atomic war work was concentrated in North America Chadwick served on the international technical committee. Later he led a contingent of British scientists to Los Alamos, New Mexico, to work on the manufacture of the A-bomb.

NIELS BOHR
(1885–   )

Splitting the Nucleus in Two

'I, NIELS HENRIK DAVID BOHR, son of professor of physiology at the University of Copenhagen, Christian Bohr, and wife, Ellen née Adler, was born October 7, 1885, in Copenhagen.' With these words, Niels Bohr, the dean of the world's physicists, begins his 'self-autobiography.' With the characteristic modesty of the great, he tells his own story in fewer than 1,500 words! And yet Denmark, the country of his birth, could hardly boast of a more important figure. 'To help to lift only a corner of the veil which covers the truth and perhaps, so doing, to get on the track of a closer relation than the one which immediately presents itself, is all the happiness that can be given to a scientist,' he said elsewhere.

Niels Bohr was born at King Georg's Palace, 14 Ved Stranden, where, during the first years of their married life, his parents lived at the house of Niel's grandmother, Mrs. Jenny Adler. The palace was built after the fire in 179͏ and is one of the most beautiful private buildings of Copenhagen. Grandfather Adler was a merchant and banker.

Niels was the first-born. He had a brother and sister. Niels and his brother Harald attended the Gammelholm's Latin Realskole and Senior High School from which Niels graduated in 1903. Four years later he received his Bachelor of Arts degree. A photograph of the two brothers at this time shows them in frock coats ('tails'), collar, cravat, and gold chain, according to the highest fashion of the time.

Bohr went on to study physics in the University of Copenhagen, the only one in Denmark at the time, established in 1479. During his university course he was awarded a gold medal by the Danish Society of Sciences for his work on waves on fluid jets. He received his Master's degree in physics in 1909, and, two years later, his doctorate, submitting a thesis on the Investigations of the Electronic Theory of Metals. Upon his graduation from the university he obtained a grant from the Carlsberg Foundation for a study tour.

There was no better place for Bohr or anyone in physics to continue his studies than in Cambridge and Manchester, England. Bohr went to both outstanding centers for research on the structure of the atom. 'As it happened, it was in 1911, a few months before my arrival in Manchester, that Professor Ernest Rutherford, later Lord Rutherford, through his discovery of the atom nucleus, laid the foundation of an altogether novel development. My collaboration and personal ties with Rutherford, which lasted until his death in 1937 and which were valuable to me, are memories that I preserve with the deepest gratitude,' he writes.

In the summer of 1912, Niels Bohr met pretty Margretha Norlund, the daughter of a pharmaceutical chemist at Slagelse. They were married on August 12, 1912. The Bohrs had five sons, the youngest of whom, Ernest (spelled the English way instead of Ernst as in Danish) was named after Rutherford, one sign of Bohr's esteem for his great teacher and colleague.

While in Manchester, he concerned himself with the

slowing up of atomic particles in their penetration through matter. He soon realized that the emission of light and X-rays by atoms could not be explained by the old theories. According to theory held before 1900, charged particles (in this case the electron) would in emitting light, have to lose energy by radiation, which spreads in the form of waves. Furthermore, the electrons would also, according to this theory, remain circulating in the same orbit or path around the nucleus. This theory, he thought, no longer fitted the facts. In 1900 Max Planck, a German theoretical physicist, had brought forth a new idea, extended later by Einstein. According to Planck, light is always emitted or absorbed in indivisible little packets, bundles, heaps, or lumps called *photons*. It is as if the light source, acting like a machine gun, fired little bullets of light. This is known as the quantum theory of light.

When Bohr returned to Copenhagen, he continued to ponder over this matter, and realized more and more that the release of energy from a radioactive element was very similar to the emission of light. The energy given off by the atom was also in the form of packets or quanta, instead of in the form of continuous radiation. An electron changed orbits as a burst of radiant energy shot off from the atom.

The electron was not free to travel in any orbit around the nucleus; only certain orbits were possible. The orbits are like energy steps. The smallest possible one is only 1/250 millionth of an inch. The next one is four times as wide; the next is nine times as wide as the smallest; the fourth is sixteen times as wide. Only when there is an energy exchange in the atom does an electron jump by steps from one orbit to the next.

Bohr's application of the quantum idea to atomic energy fitted the experimental facts and mathematical calculations. His work completed the model describing the structure or the 'astronomy' of the atom: Rutherford's nucleus was the center; the electrons sped around it in definite orbits of established distances from the center, in the same way as the planets revolve about the sun in definite orbits.

In March, 1913, Bohr wrote to Rutherford, sending along the first chapter of the paper in which he described the constitution of the atom. Rutherford was entranced with this beautiful theory which explained so well what happens in the outer part of the atom, as he had done for the nucleus.

Bohr also wrote that he hoped to return for a short visit to Manchester to talk things over, while Rutherford made the suggestion, among others, that Bohr should be as brief in his explanation as possible, for he said: 'Long papers have a way of frightening readers. It is the custom in England to put things very shortly and tersely in contrast with the Germanic method, where it appears to be a virtue to be as long-winded as possible.'

In 1913, Bohr was appointed Assistant Professor in Physics at the University of Copenhagen. A year or so later, having obtained a leave of absence from this position, he went to England for two years, 'where as lecturer at the University of Manchester, I again enjoyed the privilege of working with Rutherford. What particularly occupied me was the further development of the quantum theory in regard to atoms, and its influence on the interpretation of the new experimental progress in the field of atom physics.'

What has all this to do with disintegration of the atom, or with radioactive transformation?

Lise Meitner, an Austrian woman working in the Kaiser Wilhelm Institute in Berlin had an answer – one which was not readily accepted at first. During atomic disintegration, an alpha particle is expelled from the nucleus, the atom thereby entering a state of electric strain; put in another way, it is in an 'excited state.' A readjustment takes place, through the shooting off of a photon from the nucleus, she held. This is a gamma ray. In passing through the atom, the gamma ray gives off all or some of its energy to one of the satellite-electrons, thus driving it out of its orbit. This pro-

cess has been described in still another way: 'a gamma ray is
an S.O.S. wireless signal from the nucleus of an atom in
distress.'

IN 1916, Bohr was made full professor at his university. It
was then that he began to work for the establishment of an
Institute for Theoretical Physics where theory and experiment could be advanced in the closest possible fashion. With
financial help from the Danish Government, the Carlsberg
Foundation, and private contributions, the Institute for
Theoretical Physics of the University of Copenhagen was
ready, by 1920, to open its doors to foreign as well as Danish
physicists. It is today one of the world's leading institutions,
and Professor Niels Bohr was its director until 1956.

In 1932, the Mathematical Institute was established in an
adjacent building. Professor Bohr writes: 'To me this also
meant a most welcome daily contact with my late brother,
Professor Harald Bohr, who was director of the Mathematical Institute until his death in 1953. From the days of our
childhood he and I had always been very close and we grew
up to share the same human and scientific interests.'

As he watched the building of the new Institute go up,
he wrote enthusiastically to Rutherford about its location
in a beautiful park on the outskirts of the city, and its proposed equipment. '. . . we hope . . . it might suit you and
Lady Rutherford to come to Copenhagen and stay with us
at the time of the festivals for the opening of the laboratory,
which I hope will take place in about a year's time from
now.' Just as confidently he was looking forward to peace.

'Here in Denmark we are of course most thankful for the
possibility which the defeat of German militarism has
opened for us to acquire the old Danish port of Slesvig, and
at the same time we feel an immense relief now the war is
finished. All here are convinced that there can never more
be a war in Europe of such dimensions; all the people have
learnt so much from this dreadful lesson, and even here in

16. *Niels Bohr as a boy (right) with his mother, his brother Harald, and his sister.*

17. *Niels (right) and Harald Bohr in January, 1907, smartly dressed in the frock coats which were the fashion of the time.*

these small Scandinavian countries, where for good reasons, there certainly was not much aggressive military spirit before the war, people have got to look quite differently than before at the military side of life. . . .'

During the first ten years after the opening of the Institute (from 1920 to 1930), Bohr and his co-workers were investigating the 'ties of the electrons to the atom nuclei which determine the physical and chemical qualities of different [kinds] of matter.' It was during this period (1922) that Niels Bohr was awarded the Nobel Prize for physics, and made an honorary member of the Royal Institution and Physical Society in London, and a member of the Akademie der Wissenschaften of Berlin.

In the early 1930s, with the discovery of the neutron, the interest shifted to the nucleus, and the production of radioactive isotopes. The discovery that it was possible to transform atomic nuclei with 'atom ions' artificially accelerated to a high degree of energy opened up still another path of investigation.

During the years prior to World War II, Bohr traveled a great deal, visiting many countries not only in connection with international collaboration in physics, but 'also with a view to finding new opportunities for the many scientists who had been forced to leave their homeland and their work as a result of the political development in Europe.' During this period Einstein, Fermi, and others had come to the United States as refugees. It was only a few years later that Bohr himself had to flee from his country before the advancing Nazis.

But, early in 1939, Denmark was still a refuge for many scientists for whom Germany, Austria, and Italy had become uninhabitable. Some had gone to France and England, others to America. Two physicists in our story had escaped from Germany – Otto R. Frisch to Copenhagen and Lise Meitner, his aunt, to Stockholm. Both had been working with Otto Hahn and Fritz Strassman at the Kaiser Wilhelm

Institute in Berlin. This team of four were concentrating on a problem which had been studied for several years in both France and Italy. In all three laboratories scientists bombarded uranium with neutrons.

The Germans were now analyzing the products formed as a result of this atomic collision, and were astonished to find barium among the chemical products. Where did barium come from? The uranium nucleus has 92 protons and 146 neutrons, while barium has only 56 protons and 82 neutrons. From uranium to barium is an enormous step! Previous work had led one to expect that only small fragments, such as an electron or a positron (the same size particle of opposite charge), were chipped off, while some element close to uranium was formed. But now with the unexpected appearance of barium, something quite different must have happened. It was just at this time that Lise Meitner was forced to interrupt her work, though not her thinking about this problem.

Professor Meitner was Austrian. Though a Jew, she was permitted to stay in Germany, because her Austrian birth temporarily exempted her from the German anti-Semitic laws, which at first applied only to Germans. But with the invasion by the Nazis, Austria became linked to Germany, which meant that Lise Meitner could no longer remain in Berlin. Warned by friends, she made her escape to Stockholm. While there, word was sent to her by Hahn that their chemical experiments with barium were complete. But what was the meaning of their results?

Lise Meitner pondered over the strange appearance of barium in the disintegration of uranium. And a new and revolutionary idea was born! Could it be that when uranium swallowed up a neutron it split into two roughly equal chunks? This would explain the presence of barium which was about half the mass of uranium. She lost no time in bringing this idea to Frisch who was working at the Institute in Copenhagen. Bohr was about to leave for Princeton to discuss some theoretical problems with Einstein. He was so excited over Meitner's idea that he could hardly tear himself away in time to make the train that was to take him to the *Drottingham* for his trip to America.

In the meantime Frisch and Meitner got to work in the laboratory to test this exciting idea by experiment.

Their explanation of what happened went somewhat along these lines: The uranium nucleus behaves like the particles in a drop of liquid. If the drop is disturbed it gets into tremendous motion, and if the motion is violent enough through the addition of energy, it divides into smaller drops. 'It seems therefore possible that the uranium nucleus has only a small stability of form, and may, after neutron capture, divide itself into two nuclei of roughly equal size,' was Meitner's explanation. When they weighed the two split parts they found them to have a total weight somewhat less than the uranium atom before splitting. The mass lost must have been converted into the energy according to Einstein's formula.

By the time Bohr arrived in the United States on January 16, 1939 there was a cable waiting for him announcing that the experiment proved the correctness of Lise Meitner's idea. The answer to the mystery of the uranium fragments was found. It was a case of *fission,* as Professor Meitner named it. Uranium had split into two pieces, just as a one-celled animal divides into two equal parts. This was indeed world-shaking news, and Bohr lost no time in spreading it to his friends at Princeton and Columbia. The excitement in the laboratories was electric. Physicists immediately entered into high-gear thinking and experimenting.

One part of the story was this: vast amounts of energy will be released from this atomic fission, according to Einstein's formula for conversion of mass into energy. But there was something even more important in the story! The two fragments were not exactly equal. Uranium has 146 neutrons, barium 82, and the other fragment (krypton) 47 –

together 129. This meant that 17 neutrons remained to be accounted for. At least some of them remained free. Was it possible that these neutrons could split more uranium, *release more neutrons* which would smash additional uranium atoms — and thus keep the thing going? Perhaps the splitting could keep on going as a chain reaction, until all the uranium would be changed to barium and krypton. Energy upon energy, upon energy! This is what caused all the excitement as the enormous possibilities of the discovery unfolded in the minds of the scientists.

The next job was to see whether neutrons are really emitted during fission. Three different groups of scientists, two at Columbia, and another in France, immediately went to work. But before we get to that, we will follow Niels Bohr back to his native land.

BOHR HAD planned to spend several months with Einstein, but events in Europe were moving with threatening speed. Two months after his landing in the United States, what was left after the dismemberment of Czechoslovakia was annexed by Hitler. Refugees from Europe brought gloom in their reports of impending events. Professor Bohr was bent with worry over the danger of possible occupation of Denmark and disaster for his family. He decided to cut his visit short. Later events proved that his worries were not unfounded.

Denmark was indeed invaded by the Nazis the year after he returned to Copenhagen. During the early part of the German occupation he was able to continue his work, though with increasing difficulties. In 1943, Bohr learned from the Danish police of German plans for his imprisonment. 'I succeeded in escaping to Sweden with all my family helped by our resistance organizations.' In a small boat they crossed the Sound to Sweden.

Among the cherished possessions left behind in the laboratory were a bottle of heavy water and his gold Nobel

Prize medal. To keep the Germans from getting the precious heavy water he kept it in a beer bottle in the refrigerator. He took the bottle with him, but discovered on his arrival in Sweden that in his hasty departure he had taken the wrong bottle – what he had was just ordinary Danish beer! The bottle of heavy water was later rescued, but the medal remained dissolved in a flask of acid. Throughout the entire duration of the occupation it remained safe under the very nose of the enemy – a symbol of man's striving for knowledge and conquest over darkness. After the war the gold was recovered and the medal recast.

After a few days in Sweden, at the invitation of the British government, Bohr and his son Aage (also a physicist) were flown across to England in a perilous flight which almost cost Bohr's life from lack of oxygen. The work on the atomic bomb was in full swing by this time. 'The fear of being left behind was a strong incentive in various countries to explore, in secrecy, the possibilities of using such energy sources for military purposes. The joint American-British project remained unknown to me until, after my escape from occupied Denmark in the autumn of 1943, I came to England. . . . At that time I was taken into confidence about the great enterprise which had already an advanced stage.'

'Later on we went to the United States to collaborate on the great projects that had been initiated there.' This was in 1944. He and his son came to Los Alamos, to work among a galaxy of scientists gathered at Site Y in the desert of New Mexico. That Bohr was in Los Alamos was a strictly guarded secret. Had it been known that an atomic scientist of his world reputation was in this secluded place in the United States, it would not have been possible to keep the project a secret. For security reasons he went under the name of Mr. Nicholas Baker, or 'Uncle Nick,' to those who had known him well. His son Aage was given the innocuous name of Jimmy, an anonymity he never quite got used to.

From Mrs. Fermi's biography of her illustrious husband, we get a few impressions of Niels Bohr. 'One of the best-known characters on the mesa was Mr. Nicholas Baker. In the Los Alamos array of faces wearing an expression of deep thought at all hours and under all circumstances, whether the men they belonged to were eating dinner or playing charades, Mr. Baker's face stood out as the most thoughtful, the one expressing the gravest meditations. He appeared to be dedicated to a life of the intellect alone, which allowed no time for earthly concerns. . . . He was a few years older than the other scientists – close to sixty in 1944 – and all looked upon him with reverence, whether they knew him personally or not.'

But the much revered physicist wasn't always grave. There were moments when his lighter, jovial nature broke through the grief he felt at the suffering caused by the Nazis everywhere. He was a frequent visitor at the home of a British physicist who lived with his family in the apartment below the Fermis. In the course of the evening the Fermis would hear peals of laughter alternating with silences. Uncle Nick's subdued, almost whispering voice, as he told a joke did not carry upstairs, but the laughter of the amused listeners did. 'Bohr must have told many jokes, and all must have been funny,' Mrs. Fermi writes.

Then there was the time when a group at the project were hiking along a stream at the bottom of the Frijoles Canyon and stopped to look at a passing skunk, 'an animal whose strange habits are unknown in Europe. Its pretty appearance greatly delighted Uncle Nick. He squatted on his heels close to the little animal and excitedly praised it. He admired the fulness of its tail, the touches of white in its dark fur, the coquettish movements of its head. He was not aware of the dangers he was exposed to, and it took us a long time to persuade him to move away. . . .'

His physical stamina was no less striking than his humor and heartiness. 'Bohr surprised us with his agility. He could

be spry. We had to cross the stream numberless times, and
he never stopped to consider its width, or the best place to
go across it. He jumped it. And while he did so his body
straightened, his eyes glowed with pleasure. . . . We
climbed back, and Bohr was never out of breath. He maintained a good pace, and we could have gone no faster. . . .'
And then there was the time when a much younger man lent
him his skis for a while. Uncle Nick put them on, and off
he went. 'He gave himself to elegant curves, to expert snow-
plows, to dead stops at fast speeds, and to stylish jumps that
no one else on the slope could perform. He went on with
no pause for rest, with no thought for the man who had
taken his place at the bottom of the hill, ski-less.'

Bohr had come to the United States late in 1943. A
measure of the importance of his visit here can be gleaned
from Arthur Compton, a central figure in the production
of the bomb: 'It was the theoretical study by Niels Bohr . . .
that gave us our best understanding of what happens when
the atomic nucleus undergoes fission." But Bohr had
another part to play.

Among the first to be concerned with the consequences
of the discovery of atomic fission for good or evil, he saw it
as his duty to bring this to the attention of the highest
authorities. In an open letter he sent to the United Nations
in 1950, he wrote:

'For this purpose, I may quote from a memorandum
which I submitted to President Roosevelt as a basis for a
long conversation which he granted me in August 1944.'
The memorandum contained the following passages concerning the consequences of the project.

It certainly surpasses the imagination of anyone to sur-
vey the consequences of the project in years to come, where
in the long run the enormous energy sources which will
be available may be expected to revolutionize industry
and transport. The fact of immediate preponderance is,

however, that a weapon of an unparalleled power is being created which will completely change all future conditions of warfare. . . .

In view of these eventualities the present situation would seem to offer a most favourable opportunity for an early initiative from the side which by good fortune has achieved a lead in the efforts of mastering mighty forces of nature hitherto beyond human reach.

Since then Niels Bohr has never given up his persistent efforts to achieve world cooperation for the utilization of atomic energy for the good of mankind.

After the war, Bohr returned to Copenhagen. In 1947, his government accorded him an honor customarily bestowed only on royalty and heads of state. King Frederik made him a Knight of the Elephant, the ancient Danish order of chivalry.

Taking up his activities as professor at the University, he remained there until April 1956 when the age limit of seventy demanded his retirement.

'However,' he writes, 'I continue as head of the Institute, until further notice; during the post-war years considerable expansions have been effected, both in the way of experimental tools and resources. . . . It gives me profound joy to follow the steady progress in the field of atom physics that is being brought about by the younger generation here and elsewhere.'

'Not least in times of crises, the hopes of people all over the world are centred on the United Nations Organization and on its efforts to uphold the peace and safeguard human rights,' he wrote to Dag Hammarskjold, the Secretary General of the United Nations, on November 9, 1956.

As the writing of this book is being completed, the news comes of the latest and perhaps greatest tribute paid to Dr. Bohr. The granting to this humane, wise, yet humble colossus, of the first Atoms for Peace Award crowns a lifetime of devotion to peace and the welfare of mankind. 'I am deeply moved and very, very grateful for this unique appreciation of my efforts,' he wrote to Dr. James R. Killian, Jr., President of M. I. T. and chairman of the board of trustees of the awards organization.

'Seldom has a man dedicated himself more single-mindedly to the search of knowledge for the benefit of mankind than has Professor Bohr in his half-century as a scientist and teacher. The distinction you have conferred on him will offer hope and encouragement to men everywhere in the world who hold that science can be made to serve the hopes of mankind and help bring peace to the world.' — *President Eisenhower to Dr. Killian, March* 13, 1957.

THE JOLIOT-CURIES

Man-made Radioactivity

IRENE CURIE

(1897–1956)

AMONG IRENE CURIE'S cherished memories of her father
was the time when, returning from a trip, he brought her
a shining gold piece. She was six years old then. Her mother
had been ill and stayed behind while her father had gone to
England to receive a great honor bestowed upon both her
parents. The Royal Society presented them with one of its
highest awards: the Davy Medal, on which the names of
Pierre and Marie Curie were engraved. Curie, with his
usual absent-mindedness about 'small' things had mislaid it.
When he found it, what better could he do with it than
give it to his little daughter? And Iréne was most delighted
with her novel toy.

To his friends he pointed out her childish glee, saying:
'Irène adores her big new penny!'

Except for such things as a medal, her parents' world renown didn't affect Irène's early childhood. The Curies lived a simple life in their modest home in the Boulevard Kellerman. They spent most of their evenings at home. Marie usually left the laboratory in time to bathe and tuck little Irène into bed, often sitting at her bedside until she fell asleep. When she was a baby, her mother took her for airings, and with the joy and pride of every mother kept a record of when she got her first tooth, and when the fifteenth! She watched her through crawling and first walking steps, noted how she chased the cat, climbed from her chair on to the table, first cried, then later learned to laugh as she splashed in her bath.

When Irène didn't gain weight, or was ill, her mother was concerned, as any mother is. When her mother was away during the day, Irène played in the garden, enjoying the companionship of Dr. Curie, her grandfather, who lived with them and taught her so many wonderful things.

When Marie wrote to her brother in 1903 telling him about the Davy Medal and the Nobel Prize, invitations to come to America, and about the annoyance of visits from photographers and journalists she wrote in the same letter: 'My Irène is well. She is going to a little school rather far from the house. It is very difficult in Paris to find a good school for small children.'

In the summer of 1905, Mme. Curie had rented a little house in the country in the valley of Chevreuse, near Paris. From there she wrote to Mme. Jean Perrin, her closest friend, '. . . I am not very pleased with Irène, who has a lot of trouble getting over her whooping cough . . . and yet she has been in the country for three months . . . Irène now has a little bicycle and knows how to use it very well. She rides in a boy's costume and is very amusing to watch.'

By this time, Irène had a little sister, born December 6, 1904. Eve was to write later concerning their mother's devotion: '. . . even if she had been less attentive Irène would have known how to remind her. Irène was a despotic child. She took jealous possession of her mother and barely allowed the latter to care for 'the little one.' In the winter Marie made long journeys across Paris to discover the pippins and bananas which her elder child consented to eat, and without which she did not dare go home.'

And later: 'Mme. Curie also organized children's parties to amuse her shy Irène: a Christmas tree, decked out by her in garlands, colored candles and gilded nuts, was to leave great memories in the younger generation.' Eve also recalls a family outing on Easter Sunday, while they were resting in a meadow, Irène chasing butterflies with a small green net, and shouting with delight at every new colorful captive.

Irène was not quite nine when her father died. Her mother tried to shield her from the blow (Eve was too young to understand) and sent her off for several days to Mme. Perrin, whose children were Irène's companions. On the following day, she went across the garden, called for Irène where she was playing with blocks and talked to her across the railing. 'Pe' had hurt himself badly in the head, she told her, and needed rest. Irène caught nothing of the tragedy, as she returned to her game.

From Marie's diary we learn that after the funeral she told Irène everything: 'She did not understand, at first; . . . but afterward. . . . She cried a great deal at home, and then she went off to her little friends to forget. . . . She made great worried eyes over the black clothes that were brought to me. . . . Now she no longer seems to think of it at all.'

In the summer of that year, Marie rented a house at Sceaux. In the large garden, Irène had a place of her own to cultivate as she wished. Her grandfather chose to remain at their home, and so Irène continued to enjoy his rich companionship. A distant relative from Poland came to take up the post of governess and housekeeper in the Curie family.

When she became too ill to care for the children, other Polish governesses were to follow her.

But almost to his last days, it was Dr. Curie who was Irène's most intimate friend; she was the 'slow, untamed child, so profoundly like the son he had lost.' He taught her natural history and botany, passed on to her his enthusiasm for Victor Hugo. '. . . he polarized her intellectual life in a decisive way. The spiritual equilibrium of the present Irène Joliot-Curie, her horror of suffering, her implacable attachment to the real, her anti-clericalism and even her political sympathies come to her in the direct line from her grandfather,' Eve Curie wrote in 1937.

Marie had definite ideas about how she wanted to bring up her daughters: they were to learn to earn their own living, and be instructed 'above and beyond routine.' She thought it was barbarous to shut children up in poorly ventilated schoolrooms, when they should have the freedom of the out-of-doors. She wanted Irène to study well with a minimum of classroom attendance. Marie talked the matter over with her friends, and together they set up a teaching cooperative in which each of the great minds — Paul Langevin, Jean Perrin, Mme. Perrin, Marie Curie, and others — would share. Some ten boys and girls would gather for a single session each day to learn mathematics from Langevin, chemistry from Perrin, sculpting from Mme. Perrin. Others taught them literature, history, languages, natural science, and drawing.

It was Marie's turn on Thursday afternoon to teach elementary physics in her laboratory. Instead of boring manuals, there were live experiments with bicycle ball bearings, dipped in ink, describing the curves on inclining planes. In this way they learned the laws of falling bodies. The children themselves constructed a thermometer which they graduated to agree with official thermometers. Here Mme. Curie taught several future scientists, introducing them not only to the wonders of science, but also to its meticulous methods and routines. 'Don't tell me you will clean it afterward! One must *never* dirty a table during an experiment,' was her strictly enforced rule. A gossip writer wrote about this novel way of education:

'This little company which hardly knows how to read or write, has permission to make manipulations, to engage in experiments, to construct apparatus and to try reactions. . . . The Sorbonne and the building in the Rue Cuvier have not exploded yet, but all hope is not yet lost.'

Among this 'little company' Irène Curie was a scientific star. After two years in the cooperative school where Irène obtained a first-class scientific beginning of the kind unavailable in the best lyceum, she went on to the Collège Sévigné, a private school, where she received her secondary education.

By temperament and training Irène was destined to follow in her mother's footsteps. Her taste for disciplined work, her indifference to money, and her spirit of independence were implanted early. In 1911, when Marie went to Stockholm, to once again be honored by the Swedish Academy of Sciences, she took Irène with her. The fourteen-year-old girl was present at the solemn meeting when her mother received the Nobel Prize in chemistry, and where she was herself to be awarded the honor twenty-four years later.

In 1913, Marie and her daughters, in the company of a group of scientists, undertook a walking excursion in the Engadine. Among the excursionists were Einstein and his son. Mme. Curie, one of the rare persons in Europe to understand Einstein's theories, was the perfect intellectual companion for the inspired and talkative physicist. On these walks they engaged in discussions which passed way over the heads of the younger fry. When they caught something comprehensible from these conversations, out of context, they were amused no end, as for instance, when Einstein stopped suddenly, seizing Marie's arm and making his point: 'You understand, what I need to know is exactly what happens to the passengers in an elevator when it falls into emptiness.'

In August 1914, when the war broke out, the girls were spending the summer on a beach in Brittany, while Marie was working in Paris. August 1, she wrote them: 'Dear Irène, dear Eve, things seem to be getting worse: we expect the mobilization from one minute to the next. I don't know if I shall be able to leave. Don't be afraid; be calm and courageous. If war does not break out, I shall come and join you on Monday. If it does, I shall stay here and I shall send for you as soon as possible. You and I, Irène, shall try to make ourselves useful.'

Without a declaration of war, the Germans invaded France, and it seemed as though there would be no way for the mother to communicate with her children. Marie had only one thought: to serve her adopted country. She joined the medical service, and found the exact spot where her abilities could be utilized. There was almost no X-ray equipment at the front. With funds from the Union of Women of France, she set up the first 'radiological car,' an ordinary automobile with Roentgen apparatus; a mechanism driven by the motor of the car provided the necessary current.

She made arrangements for her daughters to stay with their Uncle Jacques, preparing them for a long separation should the Germans get to Paris. In September she wrote to Irène, 'If you cannot work for France just now, work for its future. . . . Do your mathematics and physics as well as you can.' But Paris was saved, and Marie sent for her daughters. Irène took a course in nursing. While their mother was making the rounds from one front to another, installing equipment and training people to use it, Irène and Eve kept house in the best way they could, continued their studies, and knitted sweaters for the soldiers.

But before long, Irène, trained by her mother in radiology, was able to operate X-ray equipment. At first, she was one of her mother's 'manipulators,' but soon she could take on missions by herself. At the same time she continued with her work toward a school certificate, and with her courses at the Sorbonne.

Disturbed over the lack of trained manipulators, Marie started a course at the Radium Institute. About twenty nurses took the first course in electricity, X-rays, practical work on anatomy and wound dressing. Irène shared in the teaching project undertaken by her mother.

By the time Irène was twenty-one there was no doubt in her mind about what she wanted her life work to be. She would become a physicist and work with radium. The great achievements of her parents didn't intimidate her, or dampen her ambition to work in the laboratory she had watched being built. In 1918 she became an assistant in the Institute. If ever a child followed in her mother's footsteps along the path of greatness and glory, it was Irène Curie, who with her illustrious husband carried forward the great tradition of the Curies.

FREDERIC JOLIOT

(1900–   )

FROM THE TIME she was born, Irène lived and breathed in an atmosphere of scientific investigation. But for Frédéric Joliot, the idea of doing research was a fond dream which he nourished in secret without much hope of realizing. As a young man he used to do experiments in a homemade laboratory rigged up in the bathroom. 'The experiments weren't always good for the tile and the wash basin,' he related afterwards. During this time he devoured everything he could find to read on the lives and work of the great

18. *Niels Bohr with his fiancée, Margrethe Norlund* (1912).

19. *Niels Bohr in his laboratory in* 1922, *the year he received the Nobel Prize for physics.*

French scientists – Pasteur and the Curies. On the bathroom wall he had pasted a picture of Pierre and Marie Curie in their laboratory. 'I set my sights very high,' he said shyly, referring to his 'pin-up' favorites. Farthest from his mind was the thought that some day he would rap on the door of the famous laboratory, and get a job as a humble laboratory technician at the Radium Institute.

Joliot's life was steeped in history, the history of his country, as Irène's was in physics. He was born in Paris, on March 19, 1900, when his father was fifty-seven and his mother forty-five. Frédéric was the last born of a family of four boys and two girls. To his late arrival in the family, Joliot attached much significance. 'I felt myself almost a contemporary of the events in the history of France, which somehow broadened my understanding. My mother described the bombing of Paris in 1870, the siege, the famine. She told me how one day a soldier wanted her kitten for his dinner. My mother reached for the soldier's sabre and threatened him if he didn't return the kitten. It is like myself telling my children about the war of 14-18. . . . [World War I]. At the age of fifteen I already had the maturity of men who have had the experience of a long lifetime.' His mother died at the age of eighty-seven, after having seen three wars, and his father had witnessed two. From his infancy Joliot was nourished on the stories of these events, of human suffering, of resistance by the patriots to Prussian domination, all of which influenced his thinking.

His maternal grandfather had been the chief sauce maker at the Court of Napoleon III. In this position he was permanently attached to the Imperial dining room, helping with all receptions. When the guests departed, the sovereign was in the habit of discussing informally all sorts of questions with the keepers of the Court. Grandfather Roederer was taken in by these confidences and was sentimentally attached to Napoleon III. His daughter, however, was an ardent Republican, teaching her children the history of the French

Revolution, and instilling in them a love of liberty and respect for the great struggles for freedom and social justice.

'Thus,' Frédéric Joliot told, 'while I grew up in the bourgeois way of life [middle-class] I vividly sensed the contrast between this — my way of life — and that which my mother told about.'

Frédéric received the education of most middle-class boys — the kind which prepared them for a good position and a 'proper' place in society. He attended the Lycée Lakanal, where his schoolmates were not preoccupied with social questions. On the other hand, young Joliot did not accept the notion that the world had to be the way it was: he thought it was necessary to change it for the better. He was considered a radical; for all that, his frank and amicable manner made him popular; in fact, he enjoyed the confidence of many students who disagreed with him in their school discussions.

At Lakanal, sports were an important part of student life. Frédéric was a leader in football. 'At this time, I was quasi-professional in football!' he smilingly reminisced. In 1917, he was picked as a member of the team that played the English at Amiens.

When the time came for him to choose a profession he decided to be an engineer, having been interested particularly in mechanics and chemistry. There were no free schools for engineering, and most were costly. While comfortable, his family didn't have much money, his father being a hardware store owner. Joliot chose to go to the School of Physics and Chemistry of the City of Paris, where the Curies discovered radium. To prepare for the entrance examination he went first to the School of Lavoisier, a high school.

'The change from Lakanal to Lavoisier was striking. At the lycée, among the bourgeoise [wealthy] I was at the head. At Lavoisier I met the sons of workers and small merchants who studied hard because they knew that their parents had made sacrifices to give them an education. They had no

illusions! . . . At the beginning I had difficulty following.
I had one hard year, with the grades not always good. When
I was enrolled, the Director had told my father: 'With us,
you know, our boys must work. Here there aren't any papa's
sons'. . . .' At the lycée Joliot had acquired easygoing
habits. He went fishing, hunting, and even missed classes.
At Lavoisier, he took his work seriously. 'The fact is that I
had been spoiled by contact with the rich kids. I had to get
hold of myself, and I soon felt that I would return to my
real milieu.'

After having passed the entrance examinations to the
School of Physics and Chemistry, he henceforth came out first
in everything. For Professor of Physics in his first year, he
had Paul Langevin, who had an important influence not
only on his scientific but also on his social and political
destiny. 'I admired the course which he gave us, and I
admired him for his ideas on society.'

'Paul Langevin invited me to his home in the company
of his esteemed friends. I saw then that this was a rare man,
a creator. He possessed the power to transform obscurity
into clarity. Yes, it was characteristic of Langevin, that when
a group of difficult ideas passed through his brain, they
emerged with clarity and impeccable simplicity. Such a
transformation is equivalent to creation. Langevin was one
of those men (the most extraordinary of the century). He
was astonishingly like Einstein. . . .'

One of Joliot's classmates, was André Langevin, the professor's son. Years later, his son was to marry Joliot's
daughter.

In 1923, Joliot left the school with an engineering degree
with high honors, and with a major in physics and chemistry.
What was he to do with his engineering diploma, when his
interest was in scientific research? He wanted to work with
Langevin, but how? 'I admired him but I was intimidated
by him. I didn't dare to speak to him about my affairs. It
seemed to me impossible to be able to do fundamental re-

search. I wasn't well enough prepared, I told myself. I would have to go to a higher institution (Normal Supérieure). . .'

He accepted a job at the Arbed works, at Esch-on-Alzette, in Luxembourg. Steel production and exportation there were much higher than elsewhere. The salary for an engineer was high, and the working conditions good. He lived at the plant with the other workers, and as jobs go, this one was more than satisfactory. After several months he was recalled to the army. He had been mobilized in 1918, but when the armistice came he was released, and so he had taken advantage of the surcease from service to complete his studies. Now at the artillery school of Poitiers he met an old friend from the engineering school. P. Biquard and Joliot were to remain lifelong friends and colleagues after this reunion.

Biquard, completing his service in the army several months before Joliot, had gone to see Langevin about the possibility of working in his laboratory. At the same time he also discussed with his old professor the chances of Joliot joining him there in research. Langevin was at first discouraging. He explained that since Joliot had not gone to an institution of higher learning, most universities would not accept him, unless he had done something really outstanding to warrant their waiving this requirement. In the meantime, Joliot had been assigned to Aubervilliers, where as second-lieutenant he was to work on a technical project for the army.

Turned down by Langevin, he asked himself whether he hadn't better give up the idea of research and settle down to a career of engineering in metallurgy. But something happened shortly afterward to change his decided course, after all.

Langevin thought the matter over and asked to see Biquard. 'I've decided. I will take you as a laboratory helper. About Joliot, I will see Mme. Curie. She will accept him as a helper.' A few days later, Frédéric Joliot, still in his blue officer's uniform (he had not yet been demobilized), called at the Institute of Radium. He was received by a little woman in black, and somewhat distant in her manner. It was the widow of Pierre Curie. He would have to start immediately, so that he could become acquainted with his duties before the person he was replacing was due to leave. At Aubervilliers, the Colonel acceded to the request in Mme. Curie's letter to release him a few days sooner.

On arrival at the Laboratory, he met Irène Curie, the young assistant. From that moment, Frédéric Joliot's destiny was sealed.

'MY SOLE preoccupation was with work, with productive work. My task was to acquaint myself with my new calling, to make the most of my opportunity, to achieve the most in my chosen work,' he determined.

As a laboratory worker he was earning 540 francs a month (about $150 at that time). As a graduate engineer he could have earned much more, but at the Radium Institute he was getting experience as a researcher. Mme. Curie told him that if he wanted to get anywhere he would have to complete his work towards a bachelor's degree, studies which had been interrupted by his army service. Most of the workers in the laboratory were preparing for a dissertation. In the company of much younger students he presented himself for the examinations and passed, but by his own admission, with difficulty. He then went about preparing himself for his licence certificate.

During this time Irène and Frédéric became fast friends. He admired her not only for her role as a continuator of the glorious family tradition, but for her independent mind, powerful personality, her knowledge, appreciation of poetry, her simple, direct, and self-reliant manner, and her accomplishments in sports. A real athlete, she was an expert in mountain climbing and skiing.

In the fields of radioactivity, Frédéric had much to learn

from Irène at this point in his career. Irène was only too
willing to help the talented young man. She enjoyed their
stimulating conversations in the laboratory. He often accompanied her home, and on these walks they continued their
shop talk.

Then one day, on returning from an outing in the forest
of Fontainebleau, Irène calmly announced to her family
that she had married Frédéric. It was October 4, 1926. Since
the young couple came to live with the Curies, the appearance of a man in the secluded home of the three women
created quite a stir in the household. When they decided
some time later to move into an apartment of their own,
Marie was at first saddened by the thought of not having her
companion at her side every hour of the day and night. But
when she came to know her son-in-law better, and to appreciate his exceptional qualities and his boyish enthusiasm, she
was pleased with her daughter's choice of a husband, and
heartened by her happiness. Now Marie had *two* able assistants in her laboratory, to share her worries, discuss their
research, and even to bring her new ideas. The Joliots became the Joliot-Curies, when Joliot chose to attach to his
own name that of his illustrious in-laws.

The bearing of the great name wasn't at first an easy
honor for an inexperienced scientific worker. Lest he be
considered a sort of 'Prince Consort,' he had to make a name
for himself in his own right. During this brief uncomfort-
able period, his devotion to his chosen work and his love for
Irène sustained him in his momentous but trying self-prov-
ing. In 1927, the year that their daughter Hélène was born,
Joliot finished his work toward his diploma, and in 1930,
he achieved the degree of Doctor of Science, having presented a dissertation on the electrochemistry of polonium,
one of the radioactive metals discovered by Pierre and Marie
Curie.

At the laboratory, Mme. Curie maintained strict principles in her relationship with co-workers which included

not showing favoritism to her children. Not only did they have to work under the same conditions as the other researchers, but often were given no preference or special consideration in the choice of projects. The Joliot-Curies settled in a village in Brittany; with some of their friends they formed a small colony of intellectuals, which included Jean Perrin, leading French physicist and dear friend of Mme. Curie. He, like Langevin before him, interested himself in Joliot and arranged for his membership in the National Center for Scientific Research.

Irène and Fréderic had already begun their research in radioactivity, work which led them into the complexities of the atomic nucleus. Parallel work was going on in three laboratories: In Germany, Walter Bothe noticed that beryllium. a hard, silver-white metal, when bombarded with alpha particles gave off a form of radiation with what appeared to be unusual properties: Irène and Frédéric observed that the mysterious radiation produced proton tracks in a cloud chamber containing hydrogen, but the tracks didn't start from the bombarded beryllium, but rather at various places inside the chamber; the Joliot-Curies just missed following up this hot clue. But in England, James Chadwick set out to measure these 'protons without charge,' which led him to the discovery of the neutron. Twenty-five years later Chadwick, in writing about Irène's contribution to atomic science, referred to this 'very strange effect which provided the clue to the discovery of the neutron.'

In 1933, the Joliot-Curies bombarded aluminium with alpha particles emitted from polonium and obtained radioactive aluminum. Like their parents, they had money difficulties at the laboratory. Early that year they told an American reporter: 'If we had a huge electromagnet, something weighing fifty tons, something as big as the room in which we are sitting, we could discover much more about the atom – perhaps we could transmute one into another at will, including heavy metals.

Aluminium has 13 protons and an atomic weight of 27. The new substance they produced had a mass of 30 with 15 protons. This was phosphorus, but differed from ordinary phosphorus whose atomic weight is 31. Here was a phosphorus, lighter than common phosphorus, which had never been found in nature. A new artificial isotope had been produced! More exciting yet, even while the chemical tests were being done, it was 'disappearing'; during its disappearance it was radio-active. The final product that appeared after radioactive phosphorous decayed was silicon, the well-known element, which, combined with oxygen, makes up the main ingredient of sand.

This crucial experiment in artificial radioactivity gave new significance to the theory of the structure of the atomic nucleus. Most stable chemical elements when bombarded by alpha particles, and especially by neutrons, produce radioactive isotopes. The Joliot-Curies had thus shown that these transformations yield radioactive atoms which once produced, become transformed into other stable atoms, while becoming stripped of atomic particles. For example, the uranium isotope, U_{239} is created artifically by bombardment with neutrons of stable U_{238}. U_{239} being unstable becomes converted within twenty-three minutes into neptunium, and this element in turn becomes plutonium. This important process of transmutation was the basis of the preparation of plutonium for the manufacture of the atomic bomb ten years later.

A few months before she died, Marie Curie experienced the joy of seeing her children produce artifically radioactive elements, the existence of which she and her husband had discovered in nature.

Another victory: the Joliot-Curies brought supporting evidence for Einstein's formula of the interchangeability of matter and energy: certain kinds of radiation are made up of material particles, and atoms can be converted into energy.

The news of their discovery resounded around the world. In 1935, Joliot-Curie was made a member of the Legion of Honor. In the same year the pair received the Nobel Prize for chemistry for their discovery of artificial radioactivity. The prize arrived just in time to enable them to construct their country home in Sceaux, where Joliot-Curie still lives with his children, who also are physicists.

When Hélène was four years old, her proud father showed Einstein the 'particle tracks' she scratched with pencil and paper. The old man commented in his usual wry manner, 'If you don't watch out, she will become a theoretical physicist.' Both she and her brother Pierre, born in 1932, are scientists. Like her father, Hélène graduated from the School of Physics and Chemistry. She is married to Michael Langevin, grandson of Joliot's old Professor. In 1950, she was working with her husband in her father's laboratory at the College de France. Thus, the three great names in French science Curie, Joliot, and Langevin are joined in the work of their children.

In 1936, Irène, after a short term as a member in the Blum cabinet, was appointed to succeed her mother as Professor and Director of the Curie Radium Laboratory in the Sorbonne, a post she held until her death in 1956. Frédéric was appointed Professor at the College de France, in 1937, and Director of the Laboratory of Atomic Research at the National Center of Scientific Research. Here was begun a whole series of discoveries which led to the conquest of atomic energy. Many of the important early experiments on nuclear fission were carried out by the Joliot-Curies and their students. In 1938, Irène, in collaboration with Savitch, came very close to achieving nuclear fission — a year before Hahn and Strassman accomplished it.

It would be impossible, as in the case of her parents, to separate Irène's scientific achievements from those of her equally talented husband. They themselves claimed they could not distinguish which idea was whose. But it was not only in physics that she was his co-worker and companion. She shared his enduring faith in the grand role that science plays in the emancipation and betterment of mankind. She was his comfort and support during the difficult years of the war when he was playing an active and dangerous part in the French Resistance movement against the Nazis and their collaborators within France.

In 1939, Joliot-Curie, along with his co-workers – Halban, Kowarski, and Francis Perrin – were engaged in atomic research with a view toward controlling and directing atomic energy for peaceful uses. They applied for the first patent on an atomic pile, based on the transmutation of atoms in a chain reaction. Not seeking any personal advantage, they took the patent in the name of the National Center of Scientific Research, so that all of France could benefit from their work. However, before they could carry out their ideas in practice, the war was to stop this work. For the next four years Joliot was to devote his energies in a different way in the service of his country.

May, 1940, the year of the German invasion of Holland and Belgium, Joliot, a captain in the artillery and director of war research, had but one thought: How to prevent the supply of 200 liters of heavy water from getting into the hands of the Germans (heavy water was needed for the release of atomic energy). The containers with the precious liquid were hidden in the prison of Riom, while Halban and Kowarski began to set up a laboratory at Clermont-Ferrand. But when Petain surrendered to the Nazis, Halban and Kowarski, at the direction of Joliot-Curie, embarked at Bordeaux on the way to England, carrying the heavy water with them to place it at the disposal of Great Britain, where they were themselves to continue research.

In Paris, the furious Nazis questioned Joliot-Curie. 'Which boat did your collaborators leave on?' they demanded to know. Three vessels had left Bordeaux on that day, but two had been sunk by the Luftwaffe. Halban and

Kowarski were on the third. Very coolly, Joliot-Curie named one of the sunken vessels. The Germans accepted the lie, and never thought throughout the war that the heavy water had been safely brought to England by the two scientists.

Joliot called together his laboratory workers at the College de France and told them: 'The war continues in a new form. We don't know how long it will last – five, ten, or forty years. But a new kind of warfare begins today. It is much harder than a war in uniform: it exacts great patience and sacrifice. But-take my word. This kind of war, I have long heard spoken about in my family. . . .' Thus Joliot-Curie began his activity in the Resistance movement.

With Pierre Villon he organized the National Front in 1941, of which he became the president. The laboratory was converted into an arsenal of the 'Army in the night.' Twice Joliot was arrested and interrogated by the Nazis. During the entire time that France was enslaved, Joliot-Curie was a scientist in arms, and fought wherever opportunity presented itself.

In 1946, he received the *Croix de Guerre* (War Cross), and was promoted to Commander of the Legion of Honor for his activities in the Resistance. After the Liberation, Joliot-Curie was named Director of the National Center of Scientific Research, and was appointed to head the Atomic Energy Commission.

It was at this time that Joliot-Curie returned to the work he left off in 1940 – the construction of an atomic pile. The government made available to him the fort of Chatillon, which had been badly damaged during the war. The necessary repairs made, the laboratory was installed, and the mechanics, the radio electricians, and the chemists began their work in the old fort where for many generations soldiers had stood on guard. The atomic pile in construction was given the name Zoe, meaning life. As Zoe grew, she became too large for the fort, so a large steel hangar was built to hold her. The plan was to use slabs of uranium oxide which would be bombarded with neutrons. The neutrons would be slowed in their path by heavy water, and in turn would smash more uranium atoms which would set off a chain reaction releasing atomic energy.

Could this be achieved? There were skeptics, among them the American financier Bernard Baruch. When Joliot-Curie visited the United States in 1946 to attend the Atomic Energy Conference of the UN, Baruch said to him: 'You are foolhardy to think you can construct an atomic pile in France. You don't have the means; your industries are incapable of furnishing you with what you need. Hold off, you would do much better to come to the United States. Here we will give you all the means to do your work.' Joliot-Curie smiled, and returned to France.

On December 15, 1948, in the hangar at fort Chatillon, a few miles from Paris, thirty persons stood around a cube of concrete. Among them were Frédéric Joliot-Curie, Chief Commissioner of Atomic Energy, Kowarski, Guéron, Goldschmidt, and others. In a few moments they would be ready to divert the heavy water in aluminum pipes containing the bars of uranium oxide. Neither Joliot-Curie nor any of his co-workers ever doubted the final outcome, but then, something could go wrong! The theory and the calculations were in agreement. But the theory and the calculations are one thing; the experimental test is another. It is subject to human error. With hidden emotion they handled the controls and watched the instruments which recorded the development of the chain reaction. The experiment was begun at dawn; by midday the scientists were still at their posts listening to the clicking of the counters, and watching the ascent of the curve indicating the progress of the reaction.

Shortly afterwards, Joliot-Curie, his face radiant, appeared outside the hangar, and in the company of the government representative, he sent the message of victory to the President of the Council: 'We are happy to inform you that this day at 12:12, the first French atomic pile has begun to function.' The message went around the world. The New York *Herald Tribune* the next day carried the statement: 'As of yesterday, twelve minutes past noon, the Anglo-American monopoly of atomic energy ceased to exist.' And Bernard Baruch admitted that he had been wrong.

Zoe was only a sample of the future. Much larger piles, releasing hundreds of thousands of kilowatts of power, would enable France to make precious radioactive isotopes for biological and medical uses, for physics and chemistry experiments, for innumerable industrial projects.

IN THE post-war period, Irène and Frédéric Joliot-Curie took their place in the world peace movement, determined to see that scientific developments to which they had contributed so much would be used to increase the wealth and happiness of mankind.

Irène's last few years were saddened by the campaign against her husband, especially for his courageous and outspoken opposition to nuclear weapons. He was removed from his position at the head of the French Atomic Energy Commission, and her own work as Commissioner ended soon after (1951).

Their devotion to peace made them unpopular in some quarters, and for her political views Irène was rejected for membership by the American Chemical Society in 1954. On her arrival in the United States, she was held at Ellis Island before being permitted to travel in the country.

However, their staunchness in the cause of peace won the hearts of many people – scientists and non-scientists alike. Their work in physics earned them a place of glory in the history of science no less distinguished than that of Irène's parents.

ENRICO FERMI

(1901–1954)

Enter the Atomic Age

EARLY IN 1934 a Spanish scientist arrived at the Physics Laboratory at the University of Rome and asked to see '_Sua Eccellenza Fermi_,' His Excellency Fermi. He was directed with the remark: 'The Pope is upstairs.' The puzzled visitor must have thought his question was misunderstood, for the other soon added: 'I mean Fermi, of course,' a correction which didn't enlighten the visitor any further, since he didn't know that the nickname was given to Fermi by his friends who regarded him as infallible.

When the visitor reached the second floor, two men in dirty gray laboratory coats shot by him, each holding a strange object in his hand. Bewildered, he wandered about, and finding no one, returned to the second floor again only to find the two madmen again tearing down the corridor. This time he found someone to whom he could address his question, 'Could you show me to the office of _Sua Eccellenza Fermi_?' By now the two were having their third race. The

young man called out to one of them: 'Enrico, this gentleman is here to talk to you.' 'Come along,' Enrico shouted, on
the run. The perplexed Spanish visitor had nothing to do
but follow, with some misgivings, no doubt.

This is a true story which Laura Fermi tells in the biography of her husband, Enrico. There was a method to the
'madness' of Enrico Fermi and his physicist associate,
Edoardo Amaldi. Their regular runs from one end of the
corridor to the other were an essential part of an experiment
in radioactivity.

In January of that year the Joliot-Curies had announced
their discovery of artificial radioactivity. Instead of alpha
particles they were using neutrons with which to bombard
different elements. With a gram of radium lent them by the
director of the Bureau of Public Health, as a neutron source,
and homemade Geiger counters to detect the products of
disintegration, they investigated one element after another.

On the day the Spanish caller surprised Fermi and
Amaldi in their indoor race, they were carrying the irradiated substances from the room where they produced them
to the room at the other end of the hall where the Geiger
counters recorded the radiation. The haste was essential
because the radioactivity often lasted less than a minute.
The Geiger counters had to be kept away from the neutron
source, because the emitted radiation would have disturbed
the measurements had it reached the counters. So, carrying
the irradiated substance in sealed bottles, they dashed with
them to the Geiger counters before the radioactivity was
lost.

In selecting neutrons to direct their hits at the targets,
Fermi reasoned somewhat along these lines: neutrons,
having no electric charge, are neither attracted by electrons
nor repelled by nuclei; their path is much longer, their
speed and energy higher than that of alpha particles. Therefore their chances of hitting a nucleus are much greater.

The gram of radium was kept in a safe. As it disintegrated

into radon, it shot off alpha particles; when these struck certain elements they caused them to give off neutrons. The gaseous radon was led off into little bottles through complicated tubes and this was the source of the neutrons with which Fermi attempted to irradiate every element known, beginning with hydrogen. The first one to be activated was fluorine. When they got to uranium, whose atomic number is 92, they found that it not only became radioactive, but more than one element was formed.

Among these was one product with an atomic number of 93. Was this a new element? None such existed in nature; in fact, it isn't stable, and soon disappears. The Italian workers reported their findings to the *Ricerca Scientifica* in May, 1934. While they at no time claimed the discovery of a new element, the director of the laboratory, Senator Corbino, with great pride in 'his boys' announced that their work meant the production of a new element. The newspapers all over the world did the rest to spread the idea; in fact, one small sheet went so far as to say Fermi had presented a small bottle of 93 to the Queen of Italy. Fermi hastily corrected the wrong impression created by his enthusiastic director. As we now know, the true explanation of what happened was to come five years later as a result of the experiments by the German team, Meitner-Frisch.

Fermi was now almost thirty-three, married, well known as a physicist, and Professor of Theoretical Physics, Chairman of a recently formed department at the University of Rome. His designation – *Sua Excellenza* was not a title of nobility, but one which came with his election to the Royal Academy of Italy in 1929. The title of 'Excellency' was often embarrassing to him, an appendage to his name he would have liked to forget. One time, when he registered in a hotel, the manager asked: 'Are you any relation to His Excellency Fermi?' By answering that he was only a distant relative he avoided unwanted introductions to inquisitive hotel guests.

20. *Irène and Frédéric Joliot-Curie.*

21. *Enrico Fermi (center) with his brother, Giulio, and sister, Marie.*

With the title, went the pompous uniform of silver-striped trousers, jacket with shiny embroidery, a wrap-around cloak, feathered hat, and a sword. In the presence of Mussolini, he had to wear it at the inauguration of the Academy, on the seventh anniversary of the dictator's March on Rome.

ENRICO FERMI, the third child of Alberto and Ida, was born in Rome on September 29, 1901. His father, a man without formal education, starting as a worker in a railroad office, managed by his steadiness and hard work to become a division head when railroads were going through a period of rapid expansion. His mother was an elementary school teacher. Maria the eldest of the children, was two years older than Enrico, and Giulio was one year older.

Mrs. Fermi, in delicate health, found it difficult to take care of three babies so close in age. So Enrico and his brother were sent to a nurse in the country, but because of poor health Enrico was kept there after Giulio returned. Maria remembered her little brother when he rejoined the family at two and a half. He was a small, dark, frail-looking child who cried on his homecoming, finding two children he didn't know. He soon learned to accept the rather rigid authority of his mother and to love the family.

Enrico was particularly close to his brother. They played together almost exclusively, and being so close in age they were like twins in their attachment to each other. Together they also designed electric motors which worked, and made planes which amazed adults and fascinated children.

Of the two, Enrico was the less attractive, and always careless about his appearance. He had to be reminded to wash and comb his hair. His clothes were untidy, and when his mother was out with him, she often had to wash him at a street fountain. Unlike Giulio who was cheerful, affectionate, and friendly, Enrico was shy. He was not especially good in his early schooling, writing poorly, and answering questions as briefly as possible. His teacher and his mother often thought he wasn't very intelligent.

When Enrico was fourteen his brother died suddenly from a throat infection. It was a dreadful shock for the entire family, and one from which Mrs. Fermi never recovered. The children remembered that after that she was nearly always in tears. For Enrico, the loss of his only friend was a terrible blow. He was lonely and sad, but kept his grief to himself. Only study occupied his time. Perhaps his interest in science began then. He soon found no trouble keeping at the top of the class. He learned mathematics, then physics.

When he played with other boys, because he did like outdoor games, it was as if he played more for the sake of the game than for the boys, for they weren't really his friends. He read whatever books he could get hold of, but it wasn't always easy to get them. His father had few books, and Enrico didn't have much spending money to buy his own. He soon found an outdoor market which was held each Wednesday, where he would pick up bargains in old books, prints, and even antiques.

It was at the Campo dei Fiori, the flower market place, where he met Enrico Persico. A year older, he had gone to school with Giulio, but never was his friend, because no one could get between the Fermi brothers. Now, enjoying the same things, both being studious and having an interest in science, they became fast friends. Wednesday after Wednesday they would pick up books in the market and take turns reading them. One time after finishing a book on the motion of the planets, Fermi told his sister: 'And do you know, it is written in Latin. I hadn't noticed.'

As the two boys learned more and more from their reading, they began to do experiments together with whatever odd equipment they could find. One problem they worked out, even with this crude apparatus, was a remarkably accurate measurement of the magnetic field of the earth. Another was a working theory of the gyroscope which they arrived at from the spinning motion of a top.

After graduating from high school, Enrico applied for a fellowship at the Reale Scuola Normal Superiore in Pisa, a school for outstanding students modeled after the French schools of similar name. The paper on vibrating strings which he wrote on his examination so impressed the examiner in Rome, that he called him to his office to tell him he was 'exceptional.'

In November 1918, Fermi went to Pisa. He was seventeen, filled with confidence, ambition and youthful energy. World War I was just over, and a long-lasting peace was in promise. Leaving his home that had never shed the sadness of the family tragedy, and entering the gay atmosphere of a small university, Fermi enjoyed the next four carefree years as a student. He had no financial worries, his board and lodging being free. Among other talented young people he thrived on the stimulation *and* the fun of traditional student life.

'In the stories of Pisa that I later heard there was seldom any mention of study,' his wife writes. It seems he didn't need to study long hours, because he already knew a great deal of what was being taught, and he easily remembered the new work presented in the classroom. His teachers had little else to do for him except to give him the freedom of the laboratory.

In 1922, Fermi received his degree of Doctor of Physics, having written a paper on experimental work with X-rays and passing his oral examination *magnum cum laude* (with high praise). He returned to his family in Rome just a few months before Mussolini and his Black Shirts took power. Laura (Capon) Fermi, who was then fifteen, recalls the day of the March on Rome, when, without previous warning, the children were dismissed from school in the morning, and told not to linger in the streets on their way home. In a quiet section of Rome where she lived there was much commotion.

That same morning, Laura was to learn later, Enrico was in the physics building with Professor Orso Mario Corbino discussing possibilities for future study. At the end of that month, Enrico announced to his family that with the situation in his country being as grave as it was, 'young people like me will have to emigrate.' That winter Fermi went to the University of Göttingen in Germany to study with the well-known physicist, Max Born. On a fellowship from the Italian Ministry of Public Instruction, he had no immediate concern about money. He had learned to speak German, but still he felt like a foreigner.

Somehow he was not happy in Göttingen. Among the German scientists surrounding Professor Born, he began to doubt his ability as a physicist. When his scholarship was up he returned to Rome, and was teaching an elementary course in mathematics in the spring of 1924 when he met Laura.

Through mutual friends they met one Sunday afternoon in a game of soccer suggested by Enrico. 'I had never played soccer in my life and I was no tomboy,' Laura wrote later, 'but he had spoken. There was no opening left for argument, and no opportunity for complaint.' Apparently for the rest of their life together Fermi was to lead always in making plans that they were both to follow.

Laura Fermi gives her first impression of the man she was to become engaged to four years later: 'Along with my friends came a short-legged young man in a black suit and black felt hat, with rounded shoulders and a neck craned forward. In Italy a black suit means mourning for a close relative, and I learned that his mother had recently died. His hair was also black and thick, his complexion dark. In introducing him, my friends tried to impress me:

'He is a promising physicist, already teaching at the University, although he is only twenty-two.'

Since Laura was then sixteen, twenty-two seemed to her pretty old, and so the remark, calculated to give an impression of great achievement, apparently fell flat. After this chance meeting the two didn't see each other again for over two years.

Fermi went to Florence where he taught mechanics and mathematics until 1926. This time when he returned to Rome he was to stay. He was now full Professor of Physics at the University of Rome where Laura was a second-year student. He had by now achieved a reputation not only in Italy, but in foreign countries. He had already published some thirty papers, mainly in the field of theoretical physics dealing with statistics on the behavior of molecules, atoms, and electrons, radiation emission, and behavior of gases.

Senator Corbino, the head of the physics department in Rome, was no longer actively engaged in research, yet fully aware of the great boom period in atomic physics. He dreamed of setting up a great school of physics so that his country could take its part in the development of the new ideas. He proposed the establishment of a chair in theoretical physics, and was looking about for talent.

Fermi's paper on the statistical theory of gases was just out, and he was invited to join in the *concorso,* an informal examination by one's peers, in which Fermi took first place. Second on the list was a friend of his with whom he had worked in Florence. And so 'the school' was founded with these two and later a third physicist. As time went on, others were attracted by the work produced, and by the research opportunities which Corbino made available to the growing group of 'his boys.'

Laura was taking Corbino's course in electricity, given for engineers. One morning he announced that extraordinary opportunities await any serious-minded student who wants to leave engineering and enter the more promising field of physics research. He would have the personal attention and excellent training of the chairman himself. His earnest plea yielded one willing student – Edoardo Amaldi, the young man who eight years later was Fermi's running partner from one end of the corridor to the other. Amaldi was a good friend of Laura's and often came to her home for parties and socials. On one of those evenings Enrico had also come to the party.

They were acting out the story of a movie film, while one person recited the captions. As was his habit, Enrico took the lead and was the film director, assigning parts to the rest. When Laura's sister refused to be Greta Garbo, Enrico had an alternative: '. . . show the girls that we men have no false shyness. Take the role of Greta Garbo,' he directed Edoardo, who accepted it with good grace.

From this time on, Enrico and Laura met frequently and with a group of friends they climbed mountains, took trips to the country, and rode in Enrico's broken-down French convertible. In winter there was skiing. Fermi was excellent on skiis, and no one could get ahead of him on a mountain trail. He took both sports seriously, but best of all he loved tennis.

Enrico and the three young physicists who had formed the nucleus of the school under Corbino were not only colleagues, but inseparable friends, together enjoying all kinds of physical exercise. In their quieter sessions they talked of physics or mathematics – the reason why Laura's sister referred to the group as 'logarithms.'

On the morning of July, 19, 1928, in the heat of Rome (104° in the shade) a small group of relatives and close friends gathered in the bride's home before going to the City Hall. It was to be a civil wedding; Fermi was Catholic and Laura Jewish, and since neither was religiously brought up, there was to be no church wedding. Everyone was ready, but the groom had not yet arrived. When he finally did, he explained that he had put on a new shirt, and finding that the sleeves reached beyond his fingertips, he stopped to sew a big tuck in them. The wedding party proceeded to the

Campidoglio, the historical Capitol Hill, where the City Hall stands among other palaces.

Senator Corbino was Fermi's best man. One more detail: the groom had omitted to bring a bouquet for the bride, as was customary. A thoughtful relative went to the nearest florist to repair the oversight. After the ceremony came the wedding picture, and then the Fermis took off on their wedding trip.

EVENINGS, and on rainy days, Enrico became Laura's teacher in physics, but it didn't work out well. He was certain that a good teacher could explain anything, however difficult, but Laura was not persuaded that what he found crystal-clear also made sense to her. And so they soon gave up the effort. Instead, they decided that Enrico would write a textbook, and Laura would take it down from his dictation. With the proceeds of the book he hoped to supplement his professor's salary. In the fall of the next year, the first 1,000 copies came off the press. From then on he was to receive the equivalent of 15 American cents for each volume.

Back in Rome, they made their home in an apartment in a cooperative building. Laura chose the furniture, since Enrico's only interest in such things was that the chairs and table should have straight legs. He was immersed in his university work, living according to a methodical schedule, as if an alarm clock in his brain reminded him when it was time for breakfast, when to come home for his noonday meal, and when to retire.

Characteristically, he always thought in mathematical terms even when it concerned such things as storm windows. When these had to be bought he sat down with pencil and paper to calculate the amount of cold air that would come through the window fittings, and how it would affect the temperature of the apartment. The calculations over, it turned out that he was wrong after all, having misplaced a decimal point. Though this was her great husband's *first* bad error, Laura then realized that he was not infallible, as she and everyone else had thought.

When Fermi was named to the Royal Academy of Italy in 1929, they of course were pleased and excited, he less for the honor than for the peace and security to pursue his work it would afford him. Since with membership in the new Academy went also a handsome salary, one and a half times as large as that of his university post, Fermi was delighted. 'Money has the tendency of coming of its own will to those who don't look for it. I don't care for money, but it will come to me,' is what he said at the time.

In 1930 the Fermis took their first trip to the United States, Enrico having accepted an invitation to lecture during the summer months at the University of Michigan in Ann Arbor. This was Mrs. Fermi's introduction to American history. She knew vaguely that there had been a War of Independence, but nothing of the Civil War. From the name of a book, *Abraham Lincoln,* which she had seen on her father's bookshelf, she supposed (from the name 'Abraham' being Jewish) that Lincoln was the Wandering Jew. Only in 1930 did she learn about Lincoln as the Great Emancipator. Like many other foreigners she was overwhelmed with the immensity and uniqueness of New York City, its skyscrapers, subways, bridges — and its many different kinds of people.

Among the questions Americans asked them was: 'What do you think of Signor Mussolini?' At this time the Fermis thought that 'those were good times for Fascism. . . . It is true that all freedoms were progressively being abolished; that all powers were slowly concentrating in one man. But, because of their very slowness, these processes were little felt and not much opposed. The largest part of the Italian population was conditioned by the daily Fascist press hammering with great fanfare on the achievements of the Fascist regime.' However, before long they were to think otherwise.

In the summer of 1934, the Fermis visited Argentina and Brazil, where he lectured to large audiences in overflowing lecture halls. This was a tribute to both science and to Fermi personally. It was a happy and rich summer for them, and on their return in the fall they rejoined their three-year-old daughter, Nella, who had been left behind at a villa near Florence, where Laura's wealthy aunt lived.

Enrico returned to Rome alone, and he and his collaborators resumed their bombardment of metals with neutrons. The metals were in the shape of cylinders, inside of which the neutron source was placed, and the whole thing set into a lead box. One day when they were experimenting with silver, his assistants observed that the silver cylinder behaved strangely: its activity was different when the cylinder had been placed to one corner of the lead box. When, at Fermi's suggestion, they placed the cylinder on a wooden table, the objects around it seemed to influence its activity as it was irradiated. For instance a lead plate between the neutron source and the silver increased its activity slightly. When they placed a block of paraffin in the path of the neutrons, the Geiger counter clicked madly.

What was the reason for this increased activity? Fermi proposed this explanation: Paraffin has a great deal of hydrogen. Hydrogen nuclei are protons. The neutrons hit the protons in the paraffin before reaching the silver, losing part of their energy in the collision, in the way a billiard ball is slowed up when it hits a ball of the same size. The *slowed up* neutron has a better chance of being captured by a silver nucleus than a fast one which may zoom by and miss it. If paraffin slows up neutrons will water do it too? They repeated the procedure in a goldfish fountain in Corbino's garden. The goldfish were none the worse for the shower of neutrons, and went about their business unmindful of the great experiment and the excitement of the physicists. Water also increased the artificial radioactivity of silver many times!

That night they gathered in Amaldi's house to report their results in a letter to *Ricerca Scientifica*. The slowing up of neutrons was later to play an important part when the first chain reactor for the release of atomic energy was constructed. But this is getting ahead of our story, and is also getting ahead of what the scientists could foresee at the time.

The next year the Italian army invaded Ethiopa. The world was shocked; economic sanctions were placed on Italy by the League of Nations. This, plus the unsuccessful campaign, and the cost of the war, were leading the country to ruin. It had its effect on research. The group at the university was breaking up. Some left for other countries. Those who remained hadn't the heart to continue the work with the same vigor. Mussolini continued his propaganda, lulling the people with uniforms, parades, marches, and rallies into accepting the 'tightening of the belt' idea. With great ceremony the Roman women, led by Queen Elena, marched to the Altar of the Fatherland to turn in their gold wedding rings for steel ones.

By 1936, Hitler marched on the Rhineland, threatening the peace of Europe. Fermi, like every other father (there was now also Giulio, born in February, 1936) was concerned over the safety of his family. Out of compulsion to do something he bought gas masks for his wife and children. But something more immediate was to threaten them. In the spring of 1938, Hitler and Mussolini together marched in the streets of Rome to the joint salute of 'Heil' and 'Eia.' The Manifesto of Race was issued shortly afterwards: 'JEWS DO NOT BELONG TO THE ITALIAN RACE,' it said. The campaign against the Jews was on, and Laura was Jewish. When the first anti-Semitic laws were passed in the fall of 1938, the Fermis decided to leave Italy at once.

Enrico wrote letters to four American universities applying for a position. To avoid suspicion and likely censoring of the letters — all four in the same handwriting and to

America – he mailed them in four different villages outside of Rome. The Fermis were afraid that if their intentions were known their passports would be withheld.

Fermi received offers from all and accepted the one from Columbia University. He told the Italian officials that he was going to New York on a six-month visit. Had he indicated that he and his family were emigrating, they would have been permitted to take only fifty dollars each.

On November 10th a telephone call came through for Mr. Fermi from Stockholm. It was the Secretary of the Swedish Academy of Sciences announcing that Fermi had been chosen for the Nobel Prize in physics for his work on nuclear reactions affected by slow neutrons.

A month later, the Fermis, and a nursemaid for the children, left Rome. The young Italian woman owed her permit to enter the United States to the Nobel Prize; to the American consulate these two words were magic: the nurse could go along despite the fact that the Italian quota for immigrants was closed. They were now on their way to Sweden where Fermi was to receive his award.

To three-year-old Giulio the trip to Sweden couldn't have meant more than the fun of a train ride. But to Nella, who was nearly eight, the honor accorded to her father must have been terribly exciting. It's not hard to imagine how memorable the occasion must have been.

Stockholm, December 10th, the anniversary of Nobel's death: The awards are being presented to the 1938 recipients in the beautiful Concert Hall. Enrico Fermi is occupying a front seat on the stage, next to Pearl Buck who is similarly being honored for her work as a novelist. They are seated in tall chairs, with backs of gold-tooled leather and carved lion heads. Behind them are the recipients of former years; there is Dr. Harold Urey whom Nella was to get to know in America; and there is Madame Curie, twice a winner of the award. The others in full dress are the members of the Swedish Academy.

In the audience are women in evening dress and sparkling jewels; the men are in full dress, and some are wearing decorations suspended from colored ribbons. The music is appropriate to the occasion, and the speeches are long and not very meaningful to Nella, but whatever the words mean, they have something to do with her father's receiving the greatest honor a scientist can be accorded. And now the presentation.

First Pearl Buck, and then her father walk across the stage, down the four steps to the center of the first row, where King Gustavus V of Sweden has risen from his seat. The recipients walk over to shake hands with His Majesty who presents them with a medal, a diploma, and an envelope. The envelope must contain the money, $34,000, which is part of the prize, Nella correctly guesses. Now they are backing away slowly toward the stage and up the steps, still walking backwards; this is because no one ever turns his back on royalty. The honored are now back in their seats, having made the trip safely back, without tripping.

Nella's mother was to tell her later of the festivities which followed: the King's dinner where the guests ate off gold dinner plates; the night of the reception where her mother danced with the prince and rubbed elbows with gracious ladies-in-waiting and court dignitaries, and chatted with Princess Sybille.

To the world the ceremony was shown on a film strip. Newspapers headlined the event and the story of Enrico Fermi's discovery was on the front pages. But in Italy there was criticism, because in Germany and Italy the Nobel Prize was frowned upon; it was after all, a *Peace* prize, and Germans, since 1935, were not permitted to accept the award. In a Fascist newspaper the writer reported the ceremony as he had seen it in a newsreel. In the reporter's eyes Enrico committed several 'crimes.' As if it weren't enough that he had married a Jewish wife, and accepted a tainted prize, he had also worn tails instead of a uniform, had not raised his arm in Fascist salute, but instead had shaken hands with the Swedish King!

All this the Fermis left behind as they sailed to make their home in America. As they faced the Statue of Liberty and the New York skyline, Fermi said: 'We have founded the American branch of the Fermi family.'

ENRICO SOON settled himself in his new laboratory. Laboratories are pretty much the same the world over. Besides, he was at home with colleagues he had met at international conferences, and on his visits to the United States. But it was not so easy for Laura and the children. They attended strange new schools, had to learn a foreign language, make new friends, and play American games.

Laura and the nursemaid did the shopping together. The girl was better at selecting the best vegetables and the right cuts of meat, while Laura could more easily make the conversion of dollars into lire, and so could decide if the price was right. Sometimes they found an Italian-speaking clerk in a food shop, which relieved them of the necessity of buying only what they were able to ask for. Often it was easier to buy things in cans – the label helped in the selection. Shopping in dime stores was simpler, because there one didn't have to speak at all, and ordering by mail had its own special advantages for a foreigner.

During the first six months they lived in an apartment in the neighborhood of the University, but Enrico liked a house. Across the river, in New Jersey, a number of Columbia professors had joined the suburbanites in Leonia. And so one Sunday they went out there to visit the Ureys. Dr. Harold Urey, Nobel Prize winner in chemistry, was a neighborly neighbor, as well as a colleague. The Ureys had no trouble in selling the Fermis the idea of a small-town community for a family with young children. Soon the Fermis were comfortably settled in their own home on the Palisades, with a large lawn and a small pond.

Laura Fermi tells the amusing story of the lawn which neither she nor her husband knew how to care for. Urey patiently instructed them in the way of life of an American middle-class suburbanite on Sunday. 'You don your oldest clothes, and tend your garden,' he told them. 'At no time must you permit crab grass to take over,' he explained. The Fermis were eager to take on American ways in the shortest possible time, but neither knew anything of the ritual of maintaining a healthy lawn. When the first green stuff sprouted, Laura dispatched Nella with a green blade to the expert Ureys. 'Was it crab grass?' 'No, it's not crab grass; it's too early in the season,' was the answer she brought back. When weeks later Dr. Urey visited the Fermis and saw the lawn, he tried to blunt the blow. 'Do you know what's wrong with your lawn, Laura? It's *all* crab grass.' Fermi excused their failure at lawn culture with the remark, 'Why are you so concerned about crab grass? It's green, and it covers the lawn.'

The children in their own way were becoming 'Americanized.' Giulio who at first refused to speak anything but Italian, soon discovered that 'stinky' and 'lousy' aroused a response in his playmates. Or when his mother asked him to wash his hands, he had a ready answer, at the age of four: 'This is a free country, and you can't make me.'

While the Fermis were occupied with their family problems of learning the language, and getting acquainted with a vast new and wonderful country, the world was in turmoil. Almost as soon as the Fermis arrived in New York, they had gone to greet Niels Bohr when he docked there. He had much to say about the impending war in Europe, and the danger of Hitler occupying Denmark. He also brought the news of the splitting of uranium.

In his experiments five years earlier, Fermi had himself done just that, but thought the product might be a new element. What was believed to be 'element 93' turned out to be a mixture of disintegration products. Fermi now got busy repeating the Meitner-Frisch experiments. At Columbia University, Professor Pegram, Chairman of the Physics Department, Professor John R. Dunning, and soon others joined the project. There were Leo Szilard, born in Hungary and a refugee, Walter H. Zinn, a Canadian, teaching at City College and doing research at Columbia. Thanks to the invention of the cyclotron they had available to them a source of neutrons approximately 100,000 times more intense than the source Fermi had in Rome.

If one neutron splits one atom of uranium, realizing two or more neutrons, and these make four when they hit two more atoms of uranium, then eight, and so on, should it not be possible to set up a whole series of fission reactions, until all the uranaium is used up? A self-sustaining chain reaction could perhaps be set up in which an atom violently torn into two fragments could become self-perpetuating!

Within several weeks Fermi confirmed the results of the Denmark laboratory. At the same time the Joliot-Curies also confirmed them in Paris.

The world situation was such that the thought of utilizing atomic energy to make atomic weapons occurred to the scientists. The most important fact was that atomic fission had been discovered in Germany. Would the Germans follow up their advantage in trying to run battleships with atomic energy or to make deadly weapons? There was indeed cause for alarm, because from various sources it was known that the Nazis were working actively toward a nuclear chain reaction.

The ones who were exiles from Nazi oppression and therefore most alarmed were first to urge American scientists to explore the possibilities of utilizing atomic energy. Strangely enough the government and the Army were the last to react. Scientists took the initiative in sounding the alarm, but it took a long time and much effort to arouse the officials. At the same time the physicists were themselves not sure that the job could be accomplished. But scientists in several laboratories were spurred into action by the great challenge.

Just what was going on within the university walls was known only to a few. By the summer of 1940, a voluntary system of censorship was assumed by the physicists, and was to continue for the next five years. What had been going on was learned only after the A-bomb destroyed Hiroshima in August 1945. Now the story can be told.

IN MARCH 1939, Professor Pegram wrote to an Admiral in the Navy Department, introducing Enrico Fermi: 'There is no man more competent in this field of nuclear physics than Professor Fermi.' But this first alert didn't bring results.

On August 2, 1939, Szilard, Eugene Wigner from Princeton, and Edward Teller, also a Hungarian and friend of Szilard, took an automobile trip to a quiet place in Long Island where Einstein was spending a vacation. They brought with them a letter they had framed and addressed to President Roosevelt. They chose Albert Einstein as the most distinguished scientist to sign the letter which read in part:

> In the course of the last four months it has been made
> probable – through the work of Joliot in France as well as
> Fermi and Szilard in America – that it may become pos-
> sible to set up a nuclear chain reaction in a large mass of
> uranium, by which vast amounts of power and large
> quantities of new radium-like elements would be genera-
> ted. Now it appears almost certain that this could be
> achieved in the immediate future.
>
> This new phenomenon would also lead to the construc-
> tion of bombs. . . .
>
> I understand that Germany has actually stopped the
> sale of uranium from the Czechoslovakian mines which
> she has taken over. . . .

22. *Enrico Fermi (center) with Ernest Lawrence (left) and Rabi at Los Alamos Scientific Laboratory.*

23. *Enrico Fermi in* 1938, *receives the Nobel Prize from King Gustavus V of Sweden.*

On October 11th the letter over Einstein's signature was presented in person to President Roosevelt. He immediately set up the Advisory Committee on Uranium. The sum of $6,000 was appropriated for the study of uranium fission. This 'drop in the bucket' was all that was made available up to October 1940. It wasn't until December 6, 1941, the day before Pearl Harbor, that the decision to make an all-out effort in atomic energy research was anounced. Dr. Vannevar Bush was appointed director of the new Office of Scientific Research and Development to coordinate the work.

Professor Arthur H. Compton, who was put in charge of obtaining fissionable material, writes: 'It had become evident that the key man for work on the nuclear reactor was Enrico Fermi. He not only knew what needed to be done, but he had an important series of experiments in progress testing the possibility of making a chain reaction work by using a combination of uranium and graphite. I needed his counsel as to procedure.'

The job for which Fermi was needed was to construct a pile for a self-sustaining reaction. The pile was to consist of cubes of uranium in a lattice of graphite (pure carbon). Put very simply, the uranium was bombarded with neutrons from an external source. Natural uranium contains chiefly U_{238} and O.7 per cent U_{235}, the only part that is fissionable. As U_{235} undergoes fission, the neutrons produced are high-speed neutrons which are either easily absorbed by U_{238} or otherwise lost to the reaction. Besides, the fast neutrons are not as effective as slow ones in splitting more U_{235} atoms. They tend to fly off. If, however, small chunks of uranium scattered through a large block of graphite, the escaping fast neutrons are slowed up by passing through the graphite. Thus they are more likely to produce fission in U_{235}. This arrangement permits a chain reaction to take place in spite of the presence of U_{238}. This slow and controlled reaction,

not suitable for the explosion of a bomb, was the important
first step.

In 1941, this was all still a theory, a blueprint of what
should work, if all the unknowns became known, and all the
known problems could be solved. Just how much uranium
would be needed, for instance? What was the 'critical size'
of the uranium chunk which would set off the reaction?
Besides, there were dozens of problems of a non-scientific
nature – the matter of security, for instance.

After December 7, 1941, Enrico Fermi was an enemy
alien. Our country was at war. Fermi had three more years
of residence in the United States before he would be eligible
for citizenship. Could he be trusted? Professor Compton
answers the question: 'When Fermi first came to the United
States, I had some reservations as to how far we could trust
him. Gradually those who knew him best saw how completely he was motivated by respect and esteem for the freedom offered by the United States and by a desire to make
of himself and his family good citizens of their new country.
It was this that we needed to know. It was a great asset to
the entire world that we were able to use Fermi's wisdom.'

And so Fermi responded to Compton's call to Chicago,
first traveling back and forth from New Jersey to Chicago,
until his family could join him there.

Laura Fermi begins her story where we are about to end
this chapter.

'On the campus of the University of Chicago there is an
old, dilapidated structure, an imitation of a medieval castle
with turrets and battlements. It is only a facade, concealing
the west stands of a football stadium that is no longer
used. . . . The first atomic pile was erected by a small
group of scientists in a squash court under the football
stands. They worked in great secrecy, at their fastest pace,
pressed by the urgency of their aim. The Second World War
was being fought. The men in the squash court knew that
their research might make possible the development of

atomic weapons. . . . They were the first men to see matter yield its inner energy, steadily, at their will. My husband was their leader.'

Today, tourists in Chicago read the plaque on the outer wall:

ON DECEMBER 2, 1942
MAN ACHIEVED HERE
THE FIRST SELF-SUSTAINING CHAIN REACTION
AND THEREBY INITIATED THE
CONTROLLED RELEASE OF NUCLEAR ENERGY

'This is the birth certificate of the atomic era.'

HAROLD UREY
(1893–   )

Heavy Hydrogen

THE MAJOR PART of our story unfolded in Europe. The scene now shifted across the Atlantic. Here creative research could flourish. Many scientists, scattered by the upheavals in Europe, found a haven in the United States, a place to continue their work in a free atmosphere. American wealth provided the costly instruments, equipment, foundations, and research centers. In the late thirties, the United States became the mecca for scientists from the entire world.

At the same time American physicists were increasingly attacking atomic problems. Many important contributions by several brilliant young physicists had already brought promise of a great science era ahead. The year 1932 has often been called the *annus mirabilis* (the miracle year) of physical science. In England, Chadwick had discovered the neutron. Three other momentous developments came from the United States. Carl D .Anderson, a New York born physicist, working on cosmic rays, discovered a new particle of matter, the positive electron, or *positron*. The first practical *cyclo-*

tron had been developed. In the same year heavy hydrogen was separated.

Together with the cream of the crop of the world's physicists now on our side of the Atlantic, American scientists were soon to achieve world renown in the field of nuclear science.

In the fall of 1941, Professor Arthur Compton, charged with an enormous war research task, came to Columbia University, calling on two people who were to occupy top-rung places in atom bomb construction. One was Fermi who, 'stepping to the blackboard . . . worked out . . . simply and directly, the equation from which could be calculated the critical size of a chain-reacting sphere.' The other was Professor Urey who took Professor Compton to see the work on isotope separation that was going on under his direction. Various procedures were being tested, but one of these was the diffusion of gaseous uranium through a porous barrier, for the separation of the less than one percent fissionable U_{335} from the non-fissionable over 99 per cent of inactive U_{238}.

In the company of Professor Pegram, Chairman of The Physics Department of Columbia, Urey was shortly to make a trip to England, where they were to see the work of the British at first hand. But more than the information on uranium separation, they brought back a sense of urgency that prevailed there. In Norway the Germans had taken possession of the only large factory of the world for the production of heavy water. There could be only one reason for their wanting heavy water – to use it as a moderator for slowing up neutrons in a uranium chain reaction. Fermi had used graphite as a moderator, but Urey was preparing heavy water in case this would become necessary. So were the British and the French.

In the story of the atom bomb, Urey's name is associated with both the production of heavy water and the successful separation of uranium isotopes by the diffusion method.

Professor Urey had by this time reached the peak of his brilliant career as a chemist-physicist, and had been a professor of chemistry at Columbia for twelve years.

Harold Clayton Urey was born in Walkerton, Indiana on April 25, 1893. His father was a country clergyman. When Harold was six years old his father died. His mother later remarried: his stepfather, also a clergyman, helped Harold with his early education. He attended the various schools in Indiana, graduating from high school in 1911. Circumstances did not permit him to enter college at this time, and so he took up teaching in country schools, first in his own state and later in Montana.

In 1914, he enrolled as an undergraduate at the University of Montana, and obtained his Bachelor of Science degree in 1917. It was during the first World War, when, graduating as a chemist, Urey took a position in a chemical production plant in Philadelphia. Two years in industrial chemistry convinced him that this was not the work he was cut out for. His choice of a career lay in the academic world, and he took up the post of instructor of chemistry at his alma mater.

In 1921 he entered the University of California to prepare for a doctorate in chemistry. There he worked under the direction of Dr. Gilbert N. Lewis, an inspiring teacher and a noted theorist and experimenter, who had contributed to the knowledge of the atom's structure, particularly concerning the location of its planetary electrons. Along with others he later predicted the existence of a double-weight hydrogen which would be an isotope of hydrogen. Undoubtedly, this association later led to Urey's discovery of the isotope. Urey's doctoral dissertation dealt with the properties of two-atomed gases.

Upon completion of his work in California in 1923, Urey received a fellowship from the American-Scandinavian Foundation, and went to Denmark to continue his studies at the Copenhagen Institute for Theoretical Physics under

Professor Bohr. At the end of the year he returned to the United States and became Associate in Chemistry at Johns Hopkins University, where he remained until 1929, and then moved on to Columbia.

In both universities he conducted research on the border-line of chemistry and physics, and in 1930, in collaboration with Professor Ruak, wrote a book on *Atoms, Molecules and Quanta*. From his work with different substances, studying their appearance through a spectrum, Urey had for a long time suspected the presence of *heavy hydrogen*, an isotope of ordinary hydrogen.

In the fall of 1931, F. G. Brickwedge of the United States Bureau of Standards evaporated a quantity of liquid hydrogen, and sent the last few remaining drops in a glass tube to Urey for examination. The Columbia chemist examined the sample, studying the lines of its spectrum, and in this way differentiated two kinds of hydrogen. He called the heavy hydrogen *deuterium* (D), from the Greek word meaning second.

One part in 5,000 of ordinary hydrogen is deuterium, with an atomic weight just twice as great. Ordinary hydrogen, atomic weight 1, contains one proton, one electron, and no neutron; heavy hydrogen, atomic weight 2, contains, in addition, one neutron. With oxygen it forms deuterium oxide (D_2O) or *heavy water*. (Some chemists think that heavy hydrogen should be classed as a separate element, but it is usually considered an isotope of hydrogen.)

Urey's discovery was hailed as one of the most important of the century, and in 1934 he was awarded the Nobel Prize in chemistry for it. With the later discovery of a third isotope, *tritium,* and three isotopes of oxygen, as many as eighteen different kinds of water could be formed. This opened up a brand-new world in which the possibilities of new compounds, were limitless, because hydrogen alone occurs in over 300,000 compounds. Heavy water freezes at 3.8 degrees C. instead of O degrees C. as ordinary water does.

Other of its properties also differ. For instance, tadpoles cannot live in it, and certain plant seeds will not germinate in it. Whatever other uses it could be put to, it would work as a *moderator* to slow up fast neutrons, and therefore became important in atomic research.

That heavy water could be used as a moderator was also demonstrated by Halban, the man who safely carried the supply of heavy water from Paris to England. By this time he had come to Canada, where he was continuing his experiments started in France, and later also in cooperation with the English. It explains also why the Germans were continuing to operate the heavy water factory in an isolated part of Norway, and why British commandos finally destroyed the plant in a daring raid.

In Montreal, a reactor was finally built with heavy water as the moderator, but the American group turned instead to graphite, as suggested by Fermi. Heavy water had the advantage of being free of impurities, so bothersome in graphite, but it was thought that with almost the entire world's stock of heavy water being the 165 liters (about 400 pounds) rescued from France, it would take too long to produce the several tons that were required. Therefore, in order to avoid delay in the construction of the first pile for a nuclear chain reaction, graphite was the material chosen as the most accessible moderator.

So while Urey's proposal for a large electrolytic plant for the preparation of heavy water was rejected, he was assigned another task of great importance for the continuance of his work. In the meantime, Fermi and his team (H. Anderson, Zinn, and Szilard), as well as Eugene Wigner and Edward Teller from Princeton, dismantled transportable equipment and set out for Chicago to assemble the graphite pile.

The big job that had to go on at the same time was the production of fissionable material – the separation of U_{235}. To Urey went the responsibility for developing the method of separation which was the one finally used. A method that had been worked out at Columbia for isotope separation was by diffusion of gases through a porous barrier. This was the method tried by Aston for the separation of neon-20 from neon-22, and relies on the difference in weight between U_{235} and U_{238}. The first step was to convert uranium to a compound (combined with fluorine) which normally exists as a gas.

The gas was pumped through tiny holes in a plate, the molecules containing the lighter U_{235} going through a little faster than the heavier ones of its isotope U_{238}. Once through the barrier, the gas was slightly richer in U_{235}. To make it still richer, it was passed through another barrier, and then through another for about 5,000 stages of diffusion, until a gas very rich in U_{235} was obtained. It was calculated that the barrier plates through which the gases would be pumped would have to have an area equal to several acres.

On the basis of the work at Columbia, a sketch of a complete separation plant was possible. Its cost was estimated to be some hundreds of millions of dollars, which fitted accurately the actual cost of the operation as it was later set up at Oak Ridge.

During this time, Urey was one of the small group of scientists who made up a policy committee appointed at the request of President Roosevelt, and set up under the Office of Research and Development. Its task was to see the atomic research project through to completion. When later the Army took the major responsibility, the civilian group continued with research, consultation on technical problems, and recruiting of scientific workers. When the gas diffusion method was developed to the point where it could enter into mass production of uranium, the job was transferred to an industrial firm, the Kellex Corporation.

Urey's work on the separation of isotopes didn't stop with heavy hydrogen or uranium. As director of the Substitute Alloys Materials Laboratory located at Columbia, Urey conducted research into, and developed methods for, the separation of isotopes of carbon, oxygen, nitrogen, and sulphur. Today his name is closely linked with fundamental work in this important area of chemistry.

Along with five others, Harold Urey was awarded the Congressional Medal for Merit for his war research and contributions to the production of fissionable material. He was also a member of the Scientific Panel, formed just prior to the ending of the war, whose purpose it was to advise the military on the use of the bomb. In this and in other projects he worked in close coordination with Arthur Compton who was in charge of the Metallurgical Laboratory whose work, beginning in Chicago, extended to the several centers that were established in various parts of the country.

After the war, Professor Urey joined the Institute for Nuclear Research in Chicago. His investigations reached out into entirely different areas: for instance he developed methods for the measurement of temperatures as they existed in the oceans of past geological ages. He formulated a theory for the origin of the earth, based on chemical analysis of certain cosmic elements.

At the present time Professor Urey is conducting research on cosmic rays at the Clarendon Laboratory associated with Oxford University in England.

ERNEST LAWRENCE

(1901–   )

Atom Smashing

WITH THE DEVELOPMENT of nuclear physics, scientists had to construct more and more complicated instruments. In fact, they had to invent them on an engineering scale. The horse-and-buggy stage of the individual scientist working with one or two assistants was long past. Experiments were being done by teams, and the instruments could no longer be handled by a single man.

Rutherford used alpha particles as projectiles. Eight thousand times heavier than the electron, it possessed the greatest individual energy of any particle then known. Then came the neutron which was an ideal bullet. Without charge, it was not repelled, and therefore possessed terrific penetrating power. Was it possible to make even more effective guns with which to shoot at an atomic target? Suppose it were possible to increase the speed with which atomic particles could be hurled!

This thought eventually led to the invention of a new instrument – the cyclotron, the American-born atom-smasher. With enormously speeded-up bullets the cyclotron was to provide a new way of penetrating the nucleus. Its inventor was Ernest Orlando Lawrence.

Lawrence came from the little town of Canton, South Dakota. Sixty years before he was born, his grandfather came from Norway. Ole Lavrensen, who anglicized his name to Lawrence, had been a school teacher in his native country. In the town of Madison, Wisconsin, which was then the American frontier, he settled, taking up his teaching profession. Lawrence's maternal grandfather, Eric Jacobson, came to the new land twenty years later, settling on a homestead in South Dakota, which was not yet a state.

Ernest's father, Carl G. Lawrence, graduated from the University of Wisconsin and became president of the Northern State Teachers College at Aberdeen, South Dakota. His mother was born in Canton, where the Lawrences made their home. Ernest was born there on August 8, 1901, twelve years after South Dakota became a state.

He went to the public school in Canton, and later to St. Olaf College and the University of South Dakota. Ernest showed an early interest in science, experimented with wireless communication, thought he might study medicine, but ended up by studying physics. For some of his graduate work he went to the University of Chicago where Arthur Compton, beginning his work as a young professor, was his teacher.

'He had an extraordinary gift of thinking up new ideas that seemed impossible of achievement and making them work. In our conversations in the laboratory our relations had been more those of research colleagues than those of student and teacher,' Compton writes.

In 1925, he took his doctorate at Yale University where he remained on as a Research Fellow and later as Assistant Professor of Physics. In 1926, the University of South Dakota granted him a Doctor of Science degree, and in 1928 he went to the University of California.

From a report by an obscure German physicist he learned

that the man had doubled the energy of electrical potassium ions in a vacuum tube. Lawrence got an idea. If a small voltage could be used to give repeated kicks to atomic bullets at just the right time, their speed could be increased. According to one of his professors at Yale, Lawrence 'had always shown an unusual fertility of mind and had more than his share of ideas.' Here was one he planned to put to work.

It was 1929. Like an engineer he began to sketch diagrams of the essential pieces of the apparatus, and to write down the necessary mathematical formulas. It was to be a new tool of science with which he planned to whirl an electrical bullet in a circle by bending it under the powerful influence of a giant electromagnet. Professor Compton tells how one day Lawrence visited him at Chicago to show him his plans for the cyclotron. He described it to him as an electric motor, in which a stream of atomic particles revolved with ever greater speed. When they gained enough speed, they would fly off at a selected point at the rim of the field magnet, forming a high energy 'beam.' A mighty projectile could thus be hurled at the atomic nucleus.

The first model of the new machine was a toy compared with the modern cyclotron. Yet, with only 2,000 volts, Lawrence generated a beam of hydrogen ions with energies equal to those produced with 80,000 volts. Then by 1932, with a model costing $1,000, he constructed a device with which he was able to speed protons obtained from ionized hydrogen so that they had the energy imparted by 1,200,000 volts. With this instrument he smashed the element lithium – the first artificial disintegration on this side of the Atlantic. This working model was only the beginning of the construction of giant atom-smashers.

Lawrence had by this time established himself at the University of California in Berkeley. Everyone was confident that a really powerful cyclotron could be built. A 75-ton magnet which had been built for China by the Federal Telegraph Company, to be used for radio transmission, and had never been shipped, was lying idle in California for a dozen years or more. It happened that a vice-president of the company was also a professor on the staff of the University of California, and so the magnet was turned over to the physicists, at their request. Eight tons of copper wire were used to wire it, and the electromagnet was set up in the new Radiation Laboratory at the University, with Lawrence as director.

The essential parts of the cyclotron are the immensely powerful electromagnet and an empty metal circular pan divided into two discs shaped like the letter D, also called dees. The metal pan is set between the two poles of the magnet. Particles (protons, deuterons and neutrons) are sent into the pan where they are speeded by whirling. The magnet bends their path and keeps them traveling in a circle inside the dees, which are separated by a small gap. Across this gap, several thousand volts provide the kick to send the particles around. With each electrical kick they spin ever faster. As their velocity increases, the diameter of their circular path also increases, which is another way of saying that they are sent flying toward the outer rim of the pan. By the time they reach the edge of the pan they are traveling at a speed of about 35,000 times that of a rifle bullet. At this speed they emerge as a beam from a slit, and their enormous energy is ready to bombard the target with terrific force.

The first of these merry-go-round atomic guns of any size was the 27-inch cyclotron built by Lawrence and his California team. By increasing the size of the magnet and the diameter of the pan, ever higher speeds were achieved. In 1939, Lawrence built the 60-inch cyclotron on another part of the campus. This one weighed 220 tons. The heavy hydrogen beam shot up 600,000,000 atoms per second out of the window slit of the machine at a speed of 25,000 miles per second. This was the equivalent of the disintegration effect of thirty tons of pure radium.

Lawrence didn't stop there. He designed a still larger cyclotron which hurtled particles at 60,000 miles per second, and these atomic bullets possessed the energies of over 100 million volts. By 1941, a monster magnet was buried in Charter Hill, a site near the Berkely campus. Now the control had to be handled from another building, which was connected with the cyclotron with an underground power cable. This long-distance control was necessary in order to protect operators from the powerful radiations.

As Compton points out, Lawrence possesses the boldness of 'applying large-scale engineering to scientific problems.' Another of his characteristics is to organize a team of research men to work together with enthusiasm, his 'Radiation Laboratory' at Berkeley early became a mecca for nuclear physicists and chemists from all over the world and has become increasingly so since the war. Many of these men are there to learn his techniques so they may use them in their home laboratories. 'There is more than enough research for all of us to do,' is Lawrence's motto.

Of what use are atom-smashers? They have two main uses. They can be made to produce radioactive elements. Common elements such as sodium, potassium, iodine, and phosphorus can be changed into their radioactive isotopes. While this condition of artificial radioactivity is only temporary, it is useful in treating cancer and other diseases, replacing much more expensive radium. The other use of the atom-smasher is to change one element into another. In 1940, when Lawrence was awarded the Nobel Prize, he said about the cyclotron, 'It may be the instrumentality for finding the key to the almost limitless reservoir of energy in the heart of the atom.'

Within a year and a half after Lawrence made this statement, world events were to direct his use of the cyclotron into another channel. In the fall of 1941, he telephoned Compton at Chicago to tell him that certain new developments made him believe that an atomic bomb was now possible to construct. When, shortly afterwards, they met in Chicago with James B. Conant, then President of Harvard University and chief of a committee concerned with nuclear fission research for the government, Lawrence explained what he had in mind.

The bomb could be made either from U_{235} or with a new chemical of mass 239, which was discovered in Berkeley, and was called plutonium. It was element 94. He described the method by which plutonium was converted from U_{238}.

Lawrence succeeded in convincing the two scientists of both the possibility and the necessity of going ahead with this work. In answer to the question of his own readiness to undertake work that was to take him from the many projects he was directing at the University, he answered, 'If you tell me this is my job, I'll do it.'

Lawrence had already reported on the results of the experiments at the Radiation Laboratory: element 94 (plutonium) is formed as a result of the capture of a neutron by U_{238} followed by emission of 2 electrons in a row: this new element Pu_{239} undergoes neutron fission, behaving like U_{235}. This would mean that U_{238} would be available for energy production at a much greater rate. Using element 94, perhaps 100 *pounds* would be needed where it would take possibly 100 *tons* of natural uranium. If enough element 94 were available, a chain reaction with fast neutrons would be produced, releasing energy at the explosive rate necessary for a bomb.

A few days after Compton met with Lawrence and Conant, he took the problem to Fermi at Columbia. Fermi made the calculations on the blackboard which confirmed Lawrence's idea. A hundred pounds of either U_{235} or plutonium was his conservative estimate of the amount of fissionable metal that would be needed to give a nuclear explosion. After other such discussion and meetings among scientists and government personnel, the go-ahead signal to proceed

24. *S-1 Committee and consultants at the Bohemian Grove, California,*
September, 1942.

LEFT TO RIGHT: J. R. Oppenheimer,
               Harold C. Urey
               E. O. Lawrence
               James B. Conant
               Lyman J. Briggs
               E. V. Murphree
               A. H. Compton
               R. L. Thornton
               Col. K. D. Nichols

25. *Discussion, at University of California at Berkeley, of new cyclotron proposed by Ernest Lawrence.*

LEFT TO RIGHT: E. O. Lawrence
                  A. H. Compton
                  Vannevar Bush
                  James B. Conant
                  Karl T. Compton
                  Alfred Loomis

with the work on fission research was given by Dr. Vannevar Bush, on December 6, 1941.

A committee, called S-1, which included Ernest Lawrence, was formed to undertake to study the feasibility of making atomic bombs, and to report back in six months. The argument which convinced President Roosevelt and his close advisers of the necessity of the undertaking was that if atomic bombs could be made, we must get them before the Germans did.

The members of the S-1 committee each had a specific job. Lawrence was to try to separate U_{235} by the electromagnetic method. This meant separation by means of the cyclotron. Other physicists were to use other methods. The method of magnetic separation was based on a simple enough principle: when an electrically charged particle moves across a magnetic field, the force of the magnet bends its path into the arc of a circle. With two particles of different mass moving with the same energy, the heavier one will travel in a circle of larger diameter. If U_{235} and U_{238} atoms are shot with the same energy into a magnetic field, at the farther end of the circle the two will separate. But would enough be separated to provide the many pounds that would be required? This was the method of separation that Lawrence set about to develop, at the same time that Urey was working on his.

By the spring of the next year considerable progress had been made. There were difficulties to be sure, but samples of U_{235} were already available from the magnetic separation. It seemed as though the method would work on a large scale.

In September, 1942, the S-1 Committee met at the Bohemian Grove, a park of redwood trees near San Francisco. Professor Lawrence was host to the gathering, where several important decisions were made concerning the future of the operations. This was a few days before the Army would take over the responsibility for the atomic project. Among the most important decisions arrived at at this meeting was the one to set up production plants to manufacture the materials necessary for the gigantic engineering project. It had now taken on all the aspects of mass industrial production, which, except for the designing of the bomb itself, had gone beyond the research stage.

A vast plant for uranium production was set up in Oak Ridge, Tennessee. Lawrence naturally had a hand in the plans for the uranium separation works. 'I recall in particular the large hole where the immense oval magnet was to be built for the magnetic separation of the uranium isotopes. As Ernest Lawrence was showing it to me he spoke of the magnet as the race track – and that is just what it looked like. The name was symbolic, for it was this plant that was to turn out the first really significant amount of fissionable materials,' Arthur Compton writes.

In November 1943, a pilot plant for the production of plutonium started operation nearby at the Clinton Engineering Works in Tennessee. As the huge production plants took over the actual work of making the necessary materials. the role that the top scientists played shifted from that of laboratory research workers to consultants, trouble-shooters, and on-the-spot partners with industrial engineers, mechanics, and construction workers. There were many practical problems which required technical know-how for a solution. There was no time to answer the many questions which arose by the slower laboratory method. As the work went on, the answers were found as the questions came up.

There was, for instance, the windings for the huge magnet at Oak Ridge. Copper was practically unavailable, because of the many uses in other war projects. Another electrical conductor had to be found. Why not use silver? It could be borrowed from the United States Treasury. In answer to the question by the Fort Knox authorities as to how much would be needed of the silver bullion, the figure was 'about fifteen thousands tons.' The unheard of amount nearly threw the gentleman out of his seat. 'Young man, I will have you know that when we talk of silver we speak in terms of ounces.' But the half-billion dollars worth of silver was furnished and the magnet wired. All but one tenth of one per cent. of the precious metal was later recovered and returned.

In the end, the electromagnetic method proved to be too slow, and so it was shelved in favor of the gas diffusion method. Still, Lawrence's contribution was essential. Enough plutonium had been obtained to make the study of its chemical properties possible. After all, no one knew anything about this metal. Just how much would be needed to make the tests?

After many weeks of day and night operation of the cyclotron at Berkeley and another at Washington University at St. Louis, about a half milligram, the amount of a grain of salt was available. On a microscopic scale, with this tiny amount, the chemists made the tests on which the plans for the huge installation for its plant production were based!

When the weapon was finally fashioned, Lawrence was on the top team of four – the Scientific Panel of the Interim Committee – a group of civilians to advise the President if, when, and how it was to be used, and then to make plans for the further development and control of atomic energy.

ARTHUR COMPTON
(1892–   )

Master Switchman

'I WAS ONE OF A HANDFUL to whom fell the responsibility for initiating and carrying through the American wartime atomic project,' is the way Dr. Compton begins his account of the project, the greatest single scientific undertaking by any government, in which he played a star role.

When Arthur Holly Compton entered upon the atomic scene, he was Distinguished Service Professor (Physics) at the University of Chicago, having by this time achieved a place of high prominence among the world's physicists. (His brother, Karl Taylor Compton, had also blazed trails in physics.)

Both were born in Wooster, Ohio; Arthur on September 10, 1892. Their father was an ordained minister in the Presbyterian Church. Mrs. Compton came from a long line of Swiss-French-German Mennonites, a group of whom came to America during the Napoleonic wars. Pacifism was an important religious doctrine of this Protestant sect related to the Quakers. Compton's maternal grandfather was a conscientious objector during the Civil War. The community of German-speaking Mennonites settled in southwestern Ohio, near Cincinnati. Compton's mother was the first to break away from her ancestral group when she married an American of English descent. Joining her life with a minister, she devoted herself to his religious pursuits, becoming the secretary of the foreign missionary society of the local church.

Compton's father, also a doctor of philosophy in psychoology, taught philosophy at the College of Wooster, a religious college. The Compton children had been brought up in a deeply religious atmosphere, the daughter marrying a man who had served on the Presbyterian Board of Foreign Missions in his post as principal of a Christian College in India. Because of his mother's continuous contact with missionary families whose children were students at Wooster, many of Arthur's young friends were boys and girls who had visited far-away lands. His later scientific pursuits were to take him to some of these countries in the Far East.

Compton showed his scientific bent at an early age. When he was still in his teens he built a glider that flew. While in college he invented a gyroscopic airplane control. As freshman at the College of Wooster, he, like other young men, was in the throes of deciding upon a career. 'As I was beginning to work in college my father evidently saw that I was struggling over the choice of a life work. He gave me then the only counsel along this line that I can recall ever having received from him. "Arthur," he said, "to my mind there is no calling as high as that of the ministry, and no service that is as important to the lives of men and women as that of teacher; but," he added, "you seem to me to have special facility as well as special interest in the field of science. If I am not greatly mistaken, it is in science that you will find you can do your best work. What you do in this field may become a more valuable Christian service than if you were to enter the ministry or become a teacher of a missionary." '

His father's advice set him upon his course with confidence. Upon graduation from Wooster he went to Princeton, where he received his doctorate in 1916. During the next year he taught physics at the University of Minnesota, and for the following year he was research engineer at the Westinghouse Electric and Manufacturing Co. Then, like so many promising physicists, he went to Cambridge, where he studied under J. J. Thomson. In 1919 he watched Ernest Rutherford at his experiments, and several years earlier listened to his lectures when Rutherford visited Princeton and told of his discovery of the nucleus. When Arthur was still a young boy he remembers his brother Karl discussing the news of the discovery of radium. His early dreams were of some future time when he might himself study the atom's energy, and perhaps some day take part in releasing this energy to do the work of man. There are few fortunate enough to have their dreams come true as closely as Compton's did.

In 1920, Compton became Professor of Physics at Washington University in St. Louis, Missouri, where he performed experiments with X-rays. Three years later he was made professor at the University of Chicago.

In his work with X-rays he discovered that there is an increase in their wave-length as a result of collision with electrons, a phenomenon known as Compton's Effect. In the collisions between light quanta he made the assumption that light quanta possessed not only energy but something analogous to mass; this work provided experimental confirmation that light is composed of particles.

In 1927 he received the Nobel Prize (jointly with C. T. R. Wilson) for his work on radiations. In the early thirties he was doing research on cosmic rays, which took him to many parts of the earth and atop mountains to determine the way in which cosmic rays are created, and what their effects are. Between 1926 and 1927 he was a visting professor at the University of Panjab, India.

In 1939, when physicists were excited over uranium fission, Compton says that he had no more than casual interest in the subject, because his own work was in another area, and he didn't consider himself an atomic physicist. As a member of the National Cancer Advisory Council he had occasion during the next year to discuss with Lawrence the newly built cyclotron in connection with the treatment of cancer, and the matter of atomic energy began to take on a more 'vital personal significance.'

When President Roosevelt set the ball really rolling for immediate work on atomic research, Compton became a member of the S-1 Committee along with Conant, Lawrence, and Briggs. Out of funds set aside for use at the President's discretion several millions were made available. This was December 6, 1941, one day before the attack on Pearl Harbor. The S-1 Committee, with only civilians as members took over, until 1942 when the Army was brought in to take charge of the Manhattan Project, the security name given to the atomic program.

Arthur Compton was appointed as head of that part of the project which went under the name of Metallurgical Laboratory. It concerned itself with obtaining the fissionable material, and it was established at the University of Chicago. Its work soon spilled over into buildings outside the campus, including an abandoned brewery. The area was known as Site B. One of Compton's special tasks was to design the bomb itself, which at that time was a premature assignment. First things first. The immediate problem was to find the easiest and fastest way to make enough fissionable material, U_{235} or plutonium.

1942 was a year of tremendous achievement: the materials for the first reactor pile were brought to a high standard of purity; remote control instruments and machinery were developed. The sites for plants which were to manufacture the required material were found; Site X for the Oak Ridge project was acquired for uranium separation; the site for the Argonne Laboratory, twenty miles out of Chicago was chosen. This laboratory was to set up a reactor for making plutonium. The Los Alamos laboratory, where the bomb was finally constructed, was planned. And at the very end of that year the first self-sustaining chain reaction was produced! Arthur Compton, with the top team of men whom he directed, was largely responsible for sparking all these activities.

Traveling along uncharted seas, planning for all contingencies, and ready to meet yet unknown problems, scientists grappled with a multitude of problems. The pace which these intellectual giants set for themselves was matched only by their determination to get the job done, and done in time.

The matter of uranium separation – 'four horses in a race, – as Compton called it, was undertaken first. Which will it be? The electromagnetic method assigned to Lawrence, in which the cyclotron was to be used? The thermal diffusion method which depended upon the fact that lighter molecules in a liquid travel more rapidly than heavier ones when heated? Separation by centrifuging investigated by the University of Virginia, in which heavier molecules fly off to the rim of the spinning container; or the porous diffusion method started by Urey?

The last had somewhat of a head start. Enough of the material had been separated at Columbia to provide the basis for sketching a large-scale separation plant, and to estimate the cost of the program. The procedure of trying several ways at once, by different groups in different places, may have seemed wasteful, but in the end it saved what was most important – *time!* Many other problems had had to be solved in a similar way: several trails had to be blazed at once, and then the most promising followed. How were neutrons best slowed – with graphite or with heavy water as a moderator? Fermi argued for the former, Urey for the latter. The graphite pile came out first, as we know.

As the responsible leader of the Metallurgical project,

Compton often had to make momentous on-the-spot decisions. One of these concerned the location of the experimental reactor to be built by Fermi. The plan was to construct it at the Argonne Forest site, but when the time came,
the building was not completed, meaning serious delay. 'I
believe we can make the chain reaction work safely right
here in Chicago,' was Fermi's opinion. Compton's first
thought was to ask President Hutchins, the responsible
officer of the University. But would it be fair to ask one who
was in no position to judge, since he didn't even know about
the project?

Compton assumed the responsibility himself, telling
Fermi to go ahead with the experiment in the Stagg Athletic
Field. When Conant heard that the experiment was being
performed on the Chicago campus, his 'face went white.'
Brigadier General Groves, who was the Army officer
assigned to the project, rushed to the nearest telephone to
find out whether it was really impossible to use the uncom-
pleted building at Argonne. Still, Groves didn't halt the
experiment. That the element of risk was there, no one
denied, but everyone knew the need for speed.

Were these men only determined or also sure of themselves, confident in their good judgment? One would think
from the story Professor Compton tells about security meas-
ures that he really didn't expect anything dangerous to
happen. One day his mother asked what his work in
Chicago was about. Karl answered for him, somewhat in
this way: 'I can't tell you what Arthur is doing, but if one
day you read in the papers that Chicago blew up, you will
know that his experiment was a success.'

But as we know the city of Chicago, U.S.A., without blow-
ing up, became the birthplace of the Atomic Age. The first
person whom Compton called after witnessing the dramatic
turning point in man's history was Conant, at Harvard.
'Jim, you'll be interested to know that the Italian navigator
has just landed in the new world.' 'Is that so?' came Conant's

excited reply. 'Were the natives friendly?' he wanted to know. 'Everyone landed safe and happy,' Compton assured him.

Another type of judgment was required in the choice of a site for the huge separation plant. Where should it be? In the Indiana dunes on Lake Michigan, near the center of the nation's industry, or in the Tennessee Valley which had many other features to recommend it? The essential requirements of the site were lots of electric power, a tremendous water supply for cooling, a location far enough away from inhabited areas to avoid danger should an explosion accidentally occur, and near enough to adequate transportation, a climate that would permit construction work in wintertime, and remoteness from the seacoast to make enemy attack more difficult. Again Compton was to make the choice. In the spring of 1942 he and Mrs. Compton, ostensibly on a holiday at the Great Smoky Mountains, arrived at Knoxville. The Tennessee Valley site filled the bill! The eighty-square-mile area that became Oak Ridge was chosen with headquarters at the village of Clinton, where the electromagnetic separation plant was set up as the Clinton Engineering Works.

Soon the world's largest single factory housed under one roof was to go up. Shaped like the letter U, its sides were a mile long — a four-story plant that required sixty acres of roofing. Some seventy additional buildings sprawled out over several hundred acres.

During the next spring the Comptons were again in Knoxville to make arrangements for housing 75,000 workers and their families who were to move into this wilderness that became the third largest city in Tennessee. Homes, schools, churches, and shopping centers were to be built, roads had to be cut, and streets laid. Gigantic plans had to be made and innumerable details looked after. Then Mr. Holly (the name Mr. Compton was known by as the head of the Metallurgical Project) was back in Chicago, where he says, 'My wife began her job of "selling" Oak Ridge to the wives of the men who would build and work at our new pilot plant.'

As a family partner in the project, Mrs. Compton also was involved in the many undertakings. With the first influx of young scientists into Chicago, she was the one to find living quarters for them. Until a housing office could be set up, she arranged for rooms in a friend's home for the Fermi family. Meantime, Fermi's two assistants occupied the room vacated by Compton's older son who was in the Army. Other things had to be done to settle the new arrivals 'for the duration.' 'In the fall Mr. and Mrs. Arthur H. Compton . . . gave a series of parties for the newcomers at the Metallurgical Laboratory,' writes Mrs. Fermi. 'Newcomers were by then so numerous that not even in Ida Noyes Hall, the students' recreation hall, was there a room large enough to seat them all at once, so they were invited in shifts. At each of these parties the English film *Next of Kin* was shown.' (This film portrayed the dangers of spies.)

At the end of 1943, Compton's duties were about equally divided between Oak Ridge and Chicago, 'but for the morale of the enterprise it seemed important that Oak Ridge should be my base of operations. . . . Our fifteen-year-old son was in the midst of his high-school education. It was not feasible for us to leave him in Chicago.' So they found a place for him in a school for boys in North Carolina, 100 miles from Oak Ridge. To throw off suspicion, the Comptons spent part of every month at Chicago where they attended the usual faculty and social functions. When they were occasionally away, it was supposed that they were visiting their son at school. Not even members of the family knew where to reach them at Tennessee, mail being sent to Chicago and forwarded by a secretary.

In Oak Ridge they lived in one of the newly built houses which was just like the three thousand others hastily put up. Its only distinction (which made the spot in the community known as 'Snob Knob') was that it was opposite a similar one occupied by Colonel Nichols, the commanding officer of the area. Here Betty Compton did whatever any housewife would do to make their place as livable as home.

When an important decision had to be passed on. Professor Compton gathered his 'metallurgists' at a meeting. He would carry a Bible which he opened to the lines: 'And God said unto Gideon. . . .' Just as Gideon accepted God's command, so the 'metallurgists' accepted their leader's decision. But such was the necessity of the moment and the esteem in which Compton was held, that his decisions were not questioned, Mrs. Fermi relates.

'Had I been aware that the decision of moving work from Columbia to Chicago was due to Compton, I might not have grumbled. Compton was a thoughtful and considerate person, who took no step without weighing its effects on others. Perhaps because of this, whenever he expressed an opinion, it was interpreted as an order and accepted without much comment.'

Compton had more than just 'metallurgists' and their families to deal with. There were negotiations with top executives of large industrial firms who contracted for the construction work, and for supplying the vast amounts of materials for the mammoth production projects. There was, for instance, the matter of uranium procurement. At the beginning of the war, the uses of uranium were limited to the manufacture of ceramics and the production of radium. The important sources of uranium ore were Czechoslovakia, then under Nazi control, the Belgian Congo, the Canadian Northwest, and Colorado. The most available supply came from Port Hope, Canada, a few hundred tons in the form of oxide. The only uranium metal that could be bought was made by the Lamp Division of Westinghouse.

Again it was Compton who, renewing his acquaintance with a research engineer at Westinghouse, made arrangements for reducing the uranium salt to a metal. But the process was too slow to take care of the need. Work was set into motion in a number of industrial, governmental, and university laboratories for more efficient methods. Success was finally achieved by the laboratory at Iowa State College.

Then there was the vital matter of *purity* of the uranium. In order to make the metal useful in the reactor, 'poisonous' impurities had to be reduced to one part in a million. The chemists said the quickest way was to dissolve uranium nitrate in ether, but this was a tricky chemical to work with. Compton found the company which specialized in producing both ether and pure chemicals. A telephone call to St. Louis, Missouri, and the next morning arrangements were made for getting the first six tons of uranium. The remarkable thing was that by the time the government contract was ready to be signed some months later, the last of the material order had already been shipped to where it was needed.

WITH THE success of the first chain reaction the spotlight was turned on plutonium. In the neck-and-neck race between the development of uranium and plutonium, plutonium won out as the material to be used in the bomb. While the Oak Ridge plant had hardly produced enough plutonium to make the necessary chemical tests, plans were being laid for the giant reactors at Hanford, a remote site in the state of Washington. In a near-desert stretch of 600 square miles, engineers and construction workers got to work in the spring of 1943, where shortly afterwards 60,000 people were engaged at the vast undertaking. By the fall of 1944, the first of the huge Hanford piles was started up. Mr. Holly, now under the name of H. Comas, donned a new identification badge, as he shuttled back and forth from Chicago to Hanford and to Oak Ridge, meeting with scientists, conferring with engineers, signing contracts, and checking on the progress of the work, until the plutonium was being produced in large enough quantities to be weighed in tons instead of ounces.

When this happened, Compton's immediate war assignment was over. The race for the atomic weapon was on its last lap. The finish was to take place in the desert of New Mexico, but that's the subject of the next chapter.

But there was still one decision in which Compton was to play a major role. When early in June 1945, it was known that the bomb *would* explode, those responsible for its creation turned to the question of how it was to be used, or if it should be used at all.

'We were glad and proud to have had a part in making the power of the atom available for the use of man. What a tragedy it was that this power must first be used for human destruction. If, however, it would result in the shortening of the war and the saving of lives, if it would mean bringing us closer to the time when war would be abandoned as a means of settling disputes – here must be our hope and our basis for courage.'

In these words, Professor Compton gives the sense of the final report handed in by the scientific advisers to the Interim Committee. The Scientific Panel was composed of Oppenheimer, Lawrence, Fermi, and Compton. Secretary of War Henry L. Stimson, receiving the report wrote: 'The opinions of our scientific colleagues on the initial use of these weapons are not unanimous: they range from the proposal of a purely technical demonstration to that of the military application best designed to induce surrender. . . .'

Part of the responsibility of finding out just how the scientists felt about the matter rested with Compton. Various alternative proposals to exploding the bomb at a live target were made: destroying it along with all the plans used in its creation, issuing a warning that this deadly weapon was available, as a means of forcing a surrender, demonstrating its destructiveness on some uninhabited desert island for the world to see.

27. *Dr. Robert Oppenheimer and Maj. Gen. Leslie R. Groves examining the remains of the steel tower after the first atomic test bomb explosion at Alamagordo, N.M.*

26. *Arthur Holly Compton in his x-ray laboratory at the University of California.*

At the other extreme were those who saw, in its immediate use, the shortening of the war, and the saving of untold lives including those of the Japanese, whose military authorities had vowed to fight until the last man. To get a concensus, the scientific advisers obtained an opinion poll among those who knew what was going on. Oppenheimer supervised the poll at Los Alamos, Lawrence at Berkeley, and Compton at Chicago. In the Metallurgical Laboratory, 87 per cent voted for its military use. Whatever other considerations entered into the final decision, the majority opinion shown by the poll was in keeping with it.

Compton now turned his thoughts to the future of physics. How could the work of scientists now be best directed to peacetime activity? One immediate concrete answer was the establishment at Chicago of three Institutes for Basic Research: The Institute for Nuclear Studies, the Institute of Metals, and the Institute of Radiobiology. In the creation of these institutes Compton took a leading hand.

For himself, Arthur Compton saw as his peacetime job the education of the young men and women for freedom and peaceful pursuits. Advancement of knowledge for the preservation and elevation of the dignity of man, he felt, had been a war casualty. It was now time to repair the loss.

When a call came from his alma mater, Washington University, to become its Chancellor, Compton accepted the post in 1945, guiding this great institution until 1954.

J. ROBERT OPPENHEIMER

(1904–   )

The Final Test

ONE DAY IN THE LATE FALL of 1942 a strange pair drove up a winding mountain road to a school for boys, located on a mesa, some thirty miles from Santa Fe, New Mexico. A burly Army officer, and a tall, lean, round-shouldered young professor told the puzzled principal of the Los Alamos Ranch School for Boys that his school must be closed, because the Army wished to buy the site for secret work.

The uniformed man was Brigadier General Leslie R. Groves, the Army representative in charge of the Manhattan District. The young civilian who seemed to act as his guide, showing considerable familiarity with the area of Los Alamos Canyon, was Professor J. Robert Oppenheimer, who taught physics in *two* distinguished institutions in California. His father owned a ranch in the area, which accounted for his acquaintance with the school on the lonely mesa below the Jémez Hills.

Only a few weeks earlier General Groves had telephoned Oppenheimer late one night, at his home in California, say-

ing that he had just flown in from Washington, and had to see him immediately. Soon afterwards the General was seated in the Oppenheimer living room telling 'Oppie' (as he was known among his friends) that he had been selected to head up the top secret job of making the atomic bomb. The first instructions from his direct-mannered superior were: 'Tell nothing to anyone,' not even his wife.

The General spoke not only with authority, but with the knowledge that he was picking the best man for the most important job. Even before General Groves was assigned to the project, many of the preliminary plans and calculations for constructing the atom bomb had been done. Speaking about Oppenheimer's contribution to the atomic program, Compton says: 'His technical competence in theoretical physics I knew. What now impressed me was his wisdom and firmness on policy matters involving allocation of research effort and problems of personnel. After discussing it with the other members of the S-1 group, I invited Oppie to take charge of the division of our Metallurgical Project that was responsible for the design of the atomic weapons.' This was in the summer of 1942. Discussing it later with General Groves, 'We agreed that responsibility for the bomb design and construction should henceforth be transferred from myself to Oppenheimer, who would now report directly to Groves.'

During that summer Oppenheimer had spent several weeks in Chicago recruiting the best theoreticians, the key men who drew up estimates of the feasibility of the atomic bomb, how it might be made to explode, and just how effective it would be. The late-in-the-night call from General Groves could not therefore have been a great surprise to Oppie, but the extent of the assignment he was now given went way beyond the theoretical know-how of a physicist, even one as brilliant as Oppenheimer.

Site Y, as the Los Alamos project was known, required a high order of administrative ability, a talent for smooth coordination, attention to detail, inexhaustible energy, self-less zeal and devotion, and above all qualities of diplomacy, tact, and humanity in working with people under conditions of the severest strain.

General Groves, speaking to a group of his officers about the scientists on the project, was supposed to have said: 'You will have to work with the best of the world's collection of crackpots,' a light-veined way of describing the galaxy of the world's leaders in science. Accustomed to working as individuals or in small groups on projects chosen on the basis of their special interest, they were now thrown together to work as a team on a single enormously complex job involving innumerable difficulties, and a life-and-death deadline for its completion. Its successful conclusion depended in no small measure on the qualities of their leader. Oppenheimer apparently possessed these qualities. What sort of a man is he?

When Oppenheimer was called upon to carry out this gigantic war assignment he was thirty-eight, among the youngest of the leading scientists on the project. Quite apart from his youth, his background and experience, one would have thought, had not prepared him for the immensity of the task. It can be said of Oppie, as perhaps of no other of the atomic scientists, that he was born in the lap of luxury.

He was born in New York City on April 22, 1904. He was the first child of Julius and Ella, a wealthy couple who had everything they wanted of worldly goods. But more than that, young Robert's parents had the leisure, education, and the inclination to make their home a place of culture and beauty. Julius Oppenheimer, a businessman born in Germany, a gentleman of cultivated tastes, was steeped in European history, painting, architecture, and music. Mrs. Oppenheimer was an art teacher and an accomplished painter. Both had an educated love of good music. Little Robert was accustomed to hearing the great symphonies by the classical composers played in his home. His familiarity with and recognition of even obscure selections delighted his parents. Even as a young child he learned to appreciate art from paintings, prints and photographs of famous artistic works, as well as through lessons in painting given by his mother to children of friends and neighbors for the fun it gave them all.

The Oppenheimers lived on Riverside Drive, at that time the famed Rich Row of New York, facing the beautiful Hudson River. There was nothing in the way of toys, hobbies, or amusements for children that this fashionably dressed little boy couldn't have had, and did. But for the very reason that his parents were so eager to give him all the cultural things in life, and because his precocity enabled him to absorb it all, Oppenheimer missed a great deal of the fun most children have. Unusually shy, he never recalled playing with other children, or getting dirty riding a bike, bob-sledding, skating, or just being boisterous and getting into mischief. He was always well-mannered, well-behaved, well-groomed, and precociously 'grown-up.' When he was still a very young boy, he had the kind of knowledge about ancient architecture that made adults marvel, and children shy away from him. He had the disadvantage of being a child genius, which set him aside from boys of his own age, but encouraged his parents in their ambition for him to be a great man.

Before he was seven he decided he was going to be an architect rather than a baseball player, a policeman, or a motorman. The architect-to-be surrounded himself with adult books on architecture; when his interest shifted to writing verses he was given the works of classical poets. When in turn, he began collecting stamps, dried leaves and flowers, butterflies and rocks, he learned the history of countries from which the stamps came, and the Latin names, the habitat and life history of his biological specimens. An expensive German miscroscope was ordered for his use in examining whatever caught his fancy. When painting became a temporary passion, he had an artist's easel, oil paints, and sable brushes, and was taken to art exhibits.

An amusing story is told of his preoccupation with rock specimens which started at the age of five when his grandfather bought him a box of minerals. He studied the rock formations in Central Park, examined cleavage surfaces and marks of erosion, and built up a library on mineralogy. Having learned to use a typewriter, he carried on an extensive correspondence with rock experts throughout the country. One of the professors with whom he corresponded proposed him for membership in the New York Mineralogical Club. The young boy's learned, typed letters, displaying an extensive adult vocabulary, disguised the writer's age of eleven. When he was twelve he received an invitation to deliver a lecture to the Mineralogical Club. Robert wanted his father to write and offer some excuse for his not appearing, or to tell the club that he was only twelve. But Julius Oppenheimer wouldn't hear of it.

On the appointed evening the three arrived at the club meeting hall. The usher found it hard to grasp that Robert was not just accompanying his parents, but was the principal speaker, and was to occupy a seat on the platform. Introduced to the chairman by his proud father, Robert, to the amusement of his mother, assumed his rightful place at the speaker's table. The astonished audience, amused as well as amazed, burst into applause which flustered the young man – but only for a moment. Soon recovering his customary self-assurance in the company of adults, he proceeded with his prepared talk on the bedrock of Manhattan Island. His paper was later printed in one of the publications of the club.

When the time came to choose a school for the boy, it was clear that a special school had to be found for the child prodigy. What could a school for the average child offer to one who had already begun to learn foreign languages, knew how to classify bugs and plants, read books on art and architecture? Besides, his father was determined that his son's unusual capabilities should be given the fullest possible development.

Fortunately for young Oppenheimer there was a school in New York to which exceptional children could go. It was the Ethical Culture School on Central Park West which was founded by Dr. Felix Adler about a quarter of a century before Robert was born. It was organized for a handful of the brightest children in the Midtown Elementary School, and another group from the Fieldston School in Riverdale, a fashionable Westchester suburb. Its purpose was to 'help children discover and develop their unique possibilities of mind and character and to promote their growth through sensitive response to fundamental aspects of society and the culture in which they live.' The brightest children could go ahead at their own pace, and not be held back by run-of-the-mill pupils.

In addition to academic subjects, there were courses in cooking, sewing, woodwork, weaving, and other useful manual arts, because, as Dr. Adler believed, even in an industrial society many things had to be done by hand. The school was to have another kind of influence on young Oppenheimer; it welcomed children of all faiths so that they would learn to live together 'regardless of race, color and creed,' a democratic view which the school espoused and fostered. It contributed much to the shaping of Oppie's opinions, and to its influence he owed much of his wholesome aversion to all forms of discrimination.

Where his intellectual interests were concerned, the school provided the kind of nurture he thrived on. He learned to read Greek mythology, and to read the works of the Greek philosophers, poets and playwrights. For a time he was absorbed in the classics and the history of languages, learned to sing and play Greek chants and to write them down after picking out the notes on the piano. Even among his gifted schoolmates, Oppie was conspicious as a 'book-worm' and was as popular as his modern counterparts who run away with the prizes on quiz shows.

When Robert was nine, his brother Frank was born. Like an adult, he took his share of the responsibility of caring for and amusing his little brother. In adult life, when Frank also turned out to be an accomplished and well-known physicist, Oppie took a big-brother pride in his achievements.

Summers were no vacation from study for Robert. His family had a summer home on Long Island, where Oppie arranged his room more like a laboratory than a boy's room. In the surrounding country there were lots of places to explore on collecting expeditions; then the specimens had to be mounted, pressed, labeled, classified, and preserved.

One summer, his father engaged a private teacher, and fitted up a complete laboratory where the two worked on chemical experiments according to a classroom schedule. Within six weeks he completed a full year's chemistry course. After 'school hours' he and his teacher took long walks discussing events of the day, which at that time included the progress of World War I raging in Europe and threatening to involve the United States.

Oppie's conversations, from the time he was a very little boy, were on an adult level, which quite naturally excluded him from companionship with playmates of his own age. He took no part in sports or athletics. Too busy with studies, he also had no time for a normal social life. If he was lonely, exclusively in the company of adults, he apparently didn't know it. His parents, being scholarly and intellectual themselves, didn't encourage him to take part in outdoor sports, and seemed satisfied and even pleased that their boy amused himself translating poetry he wrote in French, into Greek and then into Italian to test whether the translations retained the original meter.

About the only sport Oppie enjoyed was sailing his own

boat, which his father bought him at the end of the 'vacation' chemistry course. He and his little brother used the boat to good advantage, strengthening their muscles, and acquiring a healthy suntan.

Oppie graduated at the head of his class, delivering the valedictory speech. Before deciding on the school to send him to next (which presented a problem once again), his father arranged to take him to Europe. Traveling would enrich his education and besides, would give both of them time to think about his future.

Armed with an encyclopedic fund of book knowledge, the boy was bound to derive a great deal from his trip. What he had read or seen only in pictures now took on the fuller meaning that comes with experience. Their trip took him through Greece, Italy, Germany, France, Holland, and England, but it was not the ordinary American-in-Europe tour. Young Robert studied rock formations, bringing back specimens for his collection. He dropped a rock from the Tower of Pisa, and measured the angle of the fall. He made copious notes on architecture, drew inferences about the influence of different periods of history, verified and often corrected what he read. If it weren't that he was still young, he might have followed his resolve to become a classicist, and teach the wonders of ancient civilizations.

As it turned out, he made a sudden decision one day to go to Harvard, and was enrolled in 1923, at the age of nineteen. For once, he found himself among equals. Always a brilliant conversationalist, his exceptional intellect and broad knowledge now earned for him the respect and esteem of many students and faculty. His native wit, not apparent in the precocious but nonetheless immature boy, now blossomed with the unfolding of the man. After the first year of getting acquainted, Oppie became a social personality on the campus. Like any normal undergraduate he fell right in with dormitory life – endless talk about everything from abstruse philosophy to practical politics, girls, profs, love and literature – settling the world's problems over schooners of beer and through rings of cigarette smoke.

Apart from these intellectual bouts he stayed away from clubs, societies, and fraternities. Because of his outstanding scholarship he was rushed by two fraternities but he declined because in both he was listed as a Jew. His refusal to join, he said, was based on the practice of fraternities to discriminate against Jews, Catholics, and Negroes.

Despite the fact that he took seven courses when others took four, and spent much of the time in the library, he complained to the renowned physicist, Professor Percy Bridgman, that his work was too easy. Somewhat puzzled, Bridgman permitted him to enter his graduate course in physics, where both teacher and student discovered his weakness in handling a laboratory experiment involving the use of even the simplest equipment. 'I am not a tinkerer,' is the way Oppie himself described his lesser aptitude at experimentation. It was then that he knew that his field would be theoretical physics.

Oppenheimer completed the four-year course in three, graduating *summa cum laude* and Phi Beta Kappa, the highest honors awarded an undergraduate. As a scholar he had no equal. He possessed enormous rapidity in reading, grasping abstract ideas in a flash, and apparently retaining them forever. On a fast express trip from San Francisco to New York he once read Gibbon's entire *Decline and Fall of the Roman Empire* – approximately 3,000 pages. He graduated with the highest grades ever recorded at Harvard. But typical of the early years of this intellectual giant, was the curt phrase under his photograph in the yearbook of 1926. Where others listed the clubs, teams, athletic letters, and awards, under Oppie's name there was the simple statement: 'In college three years as an undergraduate.'

Upon graduation Oppenheimer went to Cambridge. With the recommendation of his teacher and sponsor, Professor Bridgman, he had no problem finding a place in the

Cavendish Laboratory where he got to know intimately the physicists who were in the forefront of nuclear physics. Besides Rutherford, with whom he had many discussions, he struck up a close friendship with Max Born, the famed German physicist who was much impressed with Oppenheimer's mathematical mind. He urged him later in the year to go to the University of Göttingen, the leading institution in Europe for the study of higher mathematics. Only twenty-three, with a career still to be made, Oppenheimer was taken under Born's wing.

Together they worked in Cambridge and together they departed for Germany. With his unusual ability to learn languages he soon spoke German well enough to enter into theoretical discussions with German colleagues, and to engage in a gay social life of the kind he had failed to get at Harvard. At Göttingen he received his degree of Doctor of Philosophy, on the basis of a paper he wrote in collaboration with Born on a mathematical equation expressing the effect of energy on molecules. It was in this memorable year in Europe, that Oppenheimer, an equal among Europe's brilliant scientists, came out of his shell, and became the gracious cosmopolitan he is today.

In the summer he visited the University of Zurich, and then the University of Leyden in the Netherlands where he gave a lecture in Dutch, taking six weeks to learn the language, it is said. It was from the Dutch, who were greatly taken by his personal charm as well as his ability, that he got his nickname Opje.

In the next couple of years he was a Research Fellow at Harvard and at the California Institute of Technology, and a Fellow of the International Education Board of the University of Leyden. In the spring of 1929 he returned to the United States, turning down several offers to teach in distinguished universities in Europe.

After this strenuous second year in Europe he retired to a quiet, leisurely, if lonely, life on a New Mexican ranch, an

enforced interlude from activity in order to recover his
health. He had developed a cough and had lost much
weight. Always lean and gangly, he was now painfully thin.
Here he spent his time riding for miles in the daytime, reading and writing by oil lamp at night; rock collecting, mountain climbing, corresponding with his friends in Europe,
with whom he continued by mail the discussions on atomic
theory and mathematics.

It was here he donned his now famous Stetson which he
flattened into the shape that earned him his name of the
Man with the Pork-Pie Hat. He came to love the rugged,
colorful Southwest with its friendly people. Tanned by the
New Mexican sun, riding a saddle horse on regular trips to
Santa Fé for his mail, he soon became a familiar figure
among the neighboring ranches.

The next year he was to exchange the solitude of the
desert for the busy academic life in two famous institutions
on the West coast. California was the center of the most
advanced work being done in the United States at that time.
Many of the younger workers flocked there for the opportunities for research. This was about the time that Lawrence
had taken a post in the University of California, and Carl
Anderson was there doing research on cosmic rays. There is
also the California Institute of Technology at Pasadena, one
of the world's most renowned schools for scientific and
engineering courses. Both institutions offered him positions;
to their consternation he accepted both, and he was to maintain this dual connection for the next twenty years.

The once shy, withdrawn boy became a brilliantly successful teacher. His lectures were famous, and his popularity as
a professor attracted all kinds of students – those who were
advanced enough to grasp the full meaning of what he
taught, as well as those who were entranced with his manner,
originality, and brilliance, even if they didn't always follow
him. The faculty also sat in on his classes, amazed at his
eloquence, encyclopedic knowledge, and flow of ideas.

Not only *what* he was saying, but *how*, captured his listeners. Pacing up and down, gesturing, smoking one cigarette after another, covering the blackboard with complicated equations, and all the while speaking with a fluency and beauty of language, he kept his audiences spellbound. Students were known to follow him from Pasadena to Berkeley, for the term when he was due there.

But the professor himself had to learn. He often overestimated the capacity of his students. Did they really grasp all he had to tell them, in his enthusiasm? Friendly suggestions from colleagues and his own experience taught him to slow down his pace so that the students could keep up with him.

Students brought him their knotty problems which he helped them unravel. To others he suggested ideas for research and gave them full credit for the work. No less was he helpful to his colleagues who accepted his criticism, and revised their theories accordingly. It is said that he has had more influence on the theory of physics than perhaps any other American. Throughout the country there are Oppenheimer alumni upon whose work he has left an indelible stamp.

His own social life broadened. His versatility in literature, history, philosophy, poetry, architecture, geology, and natural science helped him to make friends with colleagues in other specialties. One of his close friends was Arthur Ryder, a specialist in Sanskrit, a language which Oppenheimer learned to read fluently. At weekly readings held in Ryder's home, he developed an interest in Hindu poetry and philosophy.

Young looking even today, handsome, possessed of an easy charm, and always a good talker, Oppie became known as a genial host. His house on the side of a canyon on Shasta Road became a gathering place for all sorts of intellectuals with every shade of opinion on a variety of subjects. Oppenheimer listened to new ideas with an eagerness that matched his passion for expressing his own.

In 1940, he met Katherine Puening Harrison, a graduate student at the University of California, Los Angeles. Her speciality was mycology, a branch of botany which deals with fungi. A dark-haired, attractive and animated young woman, Kitty won Oppie's heart, and they were married shortly afterwards. The Oppenheimers have two children — Peter who is sixteen, and Toni, twelve. Whether or not they will follow in their father's or mother's footsteps when they grow up, they now enjoy doing the things most normal children do in a happy family. Oppie is an affectionate and down-to-earth father and shares the robust fun of his energetic children. Their mother maintains her interest in botany, experimenting with plants in her beautiful greenhouse, at the same time caring for her beautiful though informal household, and entertaining a host of friends.

As a physicist, Oppenheimer displays the same wide range in his research as in his scholarly grasp of so many subjects outside his field. While his most enduring interest is in elementary particles, and the ultimate structure of matter, he has worked in all branches of physics: cosmic rays, astrophysics, wave and quantum mechanics, electromagnetic phenomena, and in all other phases of investigation which enlarge man's understanding of the physical world. His very versatility may account for the fact that his name isn't linked with any single area of research as are Rutherford's, Fermi's, or Urey's. For all that, by the time of the outbreak of the war, he was recognized as one of the top ten theoretical physicists of the world.

Oppenheimer put his genius to use in other ways. It is often said of him that he was the godfather at the birth of two fundamental particles: the positron and the meson. Though others discovered them and provided the experimental proof in the laboratory, Oppenheimer worked out the theory (on the basis of his own research in cosmic rays) that the meson must exist. Oppenheimer's genius for getting at the core of an idea, without necessarily working at it himself, has enabled him to serve so well as the director of the Institute of Advanced Studies, where understanding the work of others is of the first importance.

As with Arthur Compton, so with Oppenheimer, the work he was assigned was not an area of special interest. Yet, events were to prove that the choice of the man to act as commander-in-chief of the Los Alamos project was a wise one. Just what was Oppenheimer's job?

The legend is that Oppenheimer is the man who made the bomb. He would probably be the last to want it to stick, for as he would say the bomb was only a 'gadget,' a product of engineering based on well-known principles in physics worked out before the war. One atomic scientist has called him 'the master blender.' 'It took a delicate blend of theory and experiment to evolve finally the designs for a mechanism to produce an atomic explosion.'

Back in 1942, Oppenheimer and the crew of men he gathered around him drew up on paper the estimates showing that the A-bomb was feasible. He helped to select the site where the calculations were tested in practice and where the bomb was built. His next job was to recruit the best brains to carry out the assignment. Bohr, Fermi, Chadwick, Lawrence, Frisch, and Bethe were only a few of the most brilliant stars in the galaxy of men whose work Oppenheimer was to coordinate into a coherent whole. This particular job of the master blender, according to the coiner of the phrase, was to hold 'together a near critical mass of top-flight physicists – this being an accomplishment almost as neat as making the A-bomb itself.' But not only these 'long-hairs' of the white-badge crowd took his direction with respect; he was admired also by the blue-badge workers in the less distinguished posts, for he had to work with all of them.

When Oppenheimer stepped out of the train at Santa Fé early in 1943, he estimated that the operation would require some thirty workers. Under the name of Mr. Bradley, he rented office space, hired a secretary, and expected to provide living quarters for what turned out to be an initial group of a hundred persons – scientists and their families. Site Y (the name to those who were not living at Los Alamos), a spot unmarked on the map, receiving mail through Post Office Box 1663, was to have a population of 6,000 at the end of the war.

It was Oppenheimer's job to see that the homes were built to accommodate the families that kept arriving with almost every train. He had to direct the building of laboratories without explaining exactly what they were to be used for. There were all kinds of materials, apparatus, cyclotrons, betatrons, neutron accelerators, innumerable gadgets and a variety of supplies to order, receive, and assign to proper places. A school had to be provided for the children, medical facilities set up, transportation to and from the barbed-wire area arranged for, bodyguards assigned for the workers in top-secret work. All this required more organization than science, but without it only confusion would have been reaped.

To have everything come off as smoothly as it apparently did, as director he had to keep himself informed on all phases of the work whether it was how an experiment was progressing, whether a test went off as planned, or whether there was a snag in the shipment of necessary materials. During the two-and-a-half years prior to the final test, Oppenheimer slept four hours a night, keeping in touch with everyone on the inside, and receiving and making calls to Washington, Hanford, Chicago, Oak Ridge. It had to be done quietly, unobstrusively, without 'ruffling furs' and 'raising tempers.'

Some directives were minor, many decisions major. True, he had competent assistance, the selfless devotion and the enthusiastic confidence of a great team working out of a sense of urgency, but the responsibility for the successful conclusion of the event was his. 'The main decisions were made by Oppenheimer, and all proved to be correct' was the way his contribution was appraised. And there were hundreds of problems to solve. One of the main ones was to determine the critical mass size which would detonate the bomb. The big job was to unite at great rapidity two chunks of the active material, each of which would not by itself go off. There was also the size and weight of the bomb, small enough to fit into a B-29, and large enough to do its destructive work.

Another was the speed of the neutrons. In the graphite pile the object was to slow them down, to control the reaction with cadmium rods which 'dampen' the reaction by absorbing neutrons. In the bomb which explodes within a tenth of a millionth of a second, the neutrons had to be fast and free. But just how fast? There were many such questions which had to be answered first on paper, and then tested in the field. On the proper performance of each part of the process depended the success of the whole. That it all clicked we know from the fact that the mechanism was ready ahead of schedule — before the first shipment of plutonium arrived from Hanford.

The immensity and intricacy of Oppenheimer's task can only be gleaned from the few details we know of the test of the first explosion which went off without a hitch. The place was Alamogordo Desert, about a hundred miles from Los Alamos. The time, Monday, July 16, 1945, at 5: 30 A. M. For security and safety reasons the site had to be far enough from where people lived. It was Oppenheimer who chose the spot. The parts had to be delivered to Zero Hill without an accident, and without any 'leaks.' The remote control which 'pulled the switch' involved complicated wiring of a series of electronic devices, each one automatically setting off the next. The designing and construction of the steel tower on which the bomb was mounted was another job. Measurements of what takes place inside the bomb during the explosion, the amounts and kinds of energy released, the extent of the blast, the after-explosion radiations on the ground and in the air – all had to be recorded.

About a thousand observers – scientists, radiologists, meteorologists, engineers, mathematicians, explosion experts, military staff, government officials, representatives of foreign governments – invited to witness the spectacle had to be brought to this isolated spot. Throughout the previous day one after another group landed on the Alamogordo air strip, or arrived in buses and had to be conducted to Compania Hill, about twenty miles from Zero Hill. Food and camping equipment had to be provided for the night, elaborate instructions given for the visitors' conduct and safety – how their eyes and skin were to be protected, what posture they were to assume to avoid the shock from the blast.

The assignment of duties to operating personnel was worked out with the greatest care to the last detail. One unforeseen slip, one faulty instruction, and the result might have been the loss of an untold number of lives. The fact that the first atomic blast went off at the precise scheduled moment as planned is a tribute to Oppenheimer's planning and direction.

The result: '. . . all life, vegetable as well as animal, was destroyed within a radius of a mile. There was not a rattlesnake left in the region, nor a blade of grass. The sand within a radius of four hundred yards was transformed into a glasslike substance the color of green jade. . . . The tower at Zero was completely vaporized,' wrote William L. Lawrence.

HIS ASSIGNMENT over, Oppenheimer returned to his teaching posts, for, as he said, he was not an 'armaments manufacturer.' But his tremendous experience was of inestimable value to the newly set up Atomic Energy Com-

28. *Outside view of Calder Hall, England, the world's first large-scale atomic power station.*

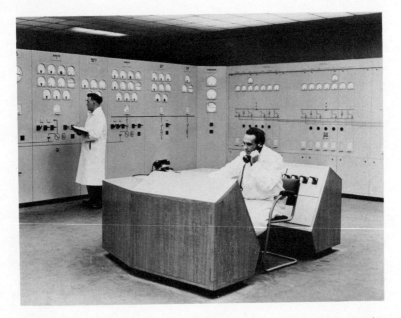

29. *Control room of the steam turbo-alternator plant at Calder Hall, showing control desk and instrument panel.*

mission. He was appointed to its General Advisory Committee, and he was called to Washington over a dozen times during the next couple of years. When these plane trips, conferences, and meetings, along with his teaching, made it impossible to continue at such a nerve-wracking pace, Oppenheimer resigned from the California institutions, and accepted the invitation to become the Director of the Institute for Advanced Studies at Princeton.

He continued his work for the Atomic Energy Commission until in 1954 the Commission's security board caused his removal because they found him a 'loyal citizen but not a good security risk' which meant that he was henceforth to be denied access to 'atomic secrets.' His colleagues demonstrated their confidence and esteem by retaining him as the honored director of the Institute where he is continuing scientific work.

INTO THE FUTURE

WHAT HAS HAPPENED to the atomic scientists since they broke camp at the end of the war? Like soldiers after battle, they were happy to return to their families and peacetime occupations. Professor Niels Bohr and Sir James Chadwick, with their contingents who came here 'for the duration,' each returned to his own country. Otto Frisch is in England, Professor at the Cavendish Laboratory. Lise Meitner is in Sweden, Max Born, retired, lives in Göttingen. Frédéric Joliot-Curie, now a widower, is applying his talents to the development of atomic industrial devices (he has recently applied for a United States patent on an atomic instrument to be used in mining and engineering).

Professor Lawrence is back in Berkeley, working at his cyclotron in the Radiation Laboratory of the University of California, constantly adding new radioactive isotopes to the growing list of thousands. Arthur Compton is Distinguished Service Professor of Natural Philosophy at Washington University: among the many organizations in which he is active is the recently formed Atoms for Peace Awards,

Inc. whose first award went to Niels Bohr. Professor Compton is also advising various government agencies in matters of atomic energy. Dr. Vannevar Bush was recently elected Chairman of the Massachusetts Institute of Technology. Harold Urey is currently working in the Fermi Institute at the University of Chicago. J. Robert Oppenheimer is Director of the Institute for Advanced Studies.

There have also been post-war casualties. Frederick Soddy, retired, died in September, 1956. Irène Curie, like her mother, was a victim of leukemia, directly attributed to her work with radioactive materials, and died on March 17, 1956. Albert Einstein, about whom President Eisenhower said: 'No other man contributed so much to the vast expansion of twentieth-century knowledge,' died as simply as he had lived, quietly passing away in his sleep on April 18, 1955. To the very end, he pursued his work on the nature of the universe, always remaining the firm pacifist who looked ahead hopefully to many peacetime promises of atomic energy. In his homely way he was wont to point out that no more than the invention of matches need the discovery of nuclear reactions bring about the destruction of mankind.

After the exodus from Los Alamos, the Fermis settled in Chicago, and he soon became a leading light in the new Institute for Nuclear Studies, where he helped to design the giant synchocyclotron, and directed the work of many younger research workers. His last scientific interest was in the most recently discovered nuclear particles – the mesons. The 'Italian navigator' who so greatly contributed to the world's emergence into a new era, recipient of the Congressional Medal for Merit, was also the first to receive the Atomic Energy Commission award of $25,000 two weeks before his death from cancer on November 28, 1954. In his honor a chair has been named in the University of Chicago; a proposed atomic power plant in Michigan will bear his name, and the 100th chemical element is called *Fermium*.

Thus each in his own way continued or continues to contribute to the ultimate realization of the work he has given to the world.

THE ATOMIC ERA is only an infant, but one with a brilliantly promising future. Plans for nuclear-fueled power stations are under way all over the world, particularly in England, Sweden, and France, where coal and oil supplies have become dangerously low, and in India and other Asiatic countries, where atomic energy offers the possibility of skipping a whole stage in the development of industry. The realization of atomic power may come sooner in these countries than in the United States, where the other fuels are still plentiful. Still, six full-scale central-station plants — in Shippingport, Pennsylvania; Chicago, Illinois; Indian Point, N. Y.; Rowe, Massachusetts; Detroit, Michigan, and Beatrice, Nebraska — are planned for operation within the next three or four years.

The principal peacetime benefit of atomic energy is undoubtedly its utilization for electric power. But if submarines can be atom-fueled, why not ships and perhaps even large planes? And how about automobiles, and household furnaces? A bit of U_{235} the size of an aspirin tablet has enough energy to drive a car four times around the earth. But is it yet feasible to dispense with gasoline and 'tank up' instead on an ounce of uranium? Scientists and engineers tell us there are problems.

For one thing, an atomic engine requires a critical mass of fuel, as if the gas tank had to be full before your car would start. For another, no matter how small it is, the engine must be encased in a heavy shield of concrete several feet thick to protect riders, pedestrians, and mechanics from dangerous radiations. Then there is the problem of the weight of atomic engines, the enormous amount of heat they generate, and the hazardous radioactive 'ashes' — the by-product of fission — that require safe disposal.

With time and continued research these problems will be solved. Meanwhile, low-power reactors and giant cyclotrons are today producing radioactive isotopes of various elements which have hundreds of uses in industry, agriculture, medicine, and research. These isotopes already are improving many industrial processes, increasing, preserving, and bettering our food supply, being used to diagnose and cure disease, and to find better and still better ways to do all of these things.

There are the 'tracers' – natural elements made radioactive – which can be followed and detected in a tobacco leaf, in cow's milk, in blood, and in the thyroid gland. Absorbed in the same way as their stable isotopes, they 'give themselves away' in the presence of a Geiger counter. Radioactive phosphorus will concentrate in a brain tumor, and radioactive iodine in diseased cells of the thyroid. Using these telltale elements, the surgeon can pinpoint many troubles.

The farmer spreads fertilizer on his soil. Will it make his corn grow taller, increase the size and number of the ears, and sweeten the kernels, or will it just make the stem grow larger? Tracers will give the answer, because the fertilizer elements can be 'tagged' and traced to the part or parts of the plant they reach. The farmer will then know how, when, and where the plant uses fertilizer. In the same way he can tell which of his calves will make good milkers.

Radioactive materials have still other uses for the farmer: they prevent the sprouting of potatoes, kill livestock pests by making the males sterile, and change the 'personality' of plants so they will resist disease, grow faster, and bring a higher yield.

These man-made elements preserve food almost indefinitely, kill larvae in meat, find leaks in pipelines, trace the trouble in an automobile engine, test the thickness of materials to 1/100,000 of an inch, and automatically control the thicknesss of metals, cloth, and plastic. They are used to sort materials, measure density, check safety devices, and measure the wear of piston rings and tires.

There is the treatment of disease: a thyroid tumor can be destroyed with injections of radioactive iodine, certain kinds of leukemia are treated with radioactive cobalt. The list of medical uses for radioactive isotopes seems to be limitless!

Finally, isotopes are being used to discover new truths, to open up ever new paths of research, including how to make more fissionable fuel and how to release energy in imitation of the sun. Some reactors (breeder type) designed especially to make plutonium with neutrons that are knocked out of uranium, actually *make* more fuel than they use. Thus far atomic energy has come from the *splitting* of *heavy* elements, but research is presently going on to release almost inexhaustible supplies of energy through the *combination* of *lighter* elements, making hydrogen into helium, the sun's way.

MAN'S creativeness is without bounds, and the potential of his achievements unending. Science, the organized use of knowledge, flourishes best in an atmosphere of peace, and with the unhampered exchange of ideas among scientists.

Perhaps our book should end on this theme, best expressed by the 'grand old man' of them all, Niels Bohr. In 1956, in a letter to Dag Hammarskjold, Secretary-General of the United Nations referring to the free exchange of knowledge among nations he wrote:

'Indeed, it is only by such co-operation that the promise for improving the welfare of peoples all over the globe, held out by the development of science, can be fulfilled and the menace to civilization arising from the new powerful means of destruction can be eliminated.'

BIBLIOGRAPHY

ANDRADE, E. N. de C.; The Birth of the Nuclear Atom, *Scientific American,* Nov. 1956, p. 93

BARNETT, LINCOLN: Oppenheimer, *Life,* Oct. 10, 1949, p. 121

BLACKETT, P. M. S.; *Atomic Weapons and East-West Relations,* Cambridge University Press, 1956

BOHR, NIELS; An Autobiogaphy, *Acta Jutlandica XXVIII,* University of Aarhaus, Jutland, Denmark

BOHR, NIELS; Letter to the Secretary General of the United Nations, Dag Hammarskjold, Nov. 9, 1956

BOHR, NIELS; *Life,* Apr. 8, 1957

BOHR, NIELS; Open Letter to the United Nations, June 9, 1950, J. H. Schultz Forlag

BROMLEY, DOROTHY DUNBAR; Two Who Carry on the Curie Tradition, *N. Y. Times Magazine,* Jan. 1933

BUSH, VANNEVAR; *Endless Horizons,* Public Affairs Press, 1946

CHADWICK, SIR JAMES; Irène Curie, *Nature,* 1177:964, May 26, 1956

COMPTON, ARTHUR HOLLY; *Atomic Quest,* Oxford University Press, 1956

CROWTHER, J. G.; *British Scientists of the Twentieth Century,* Routledge & Kegan Paul, Ltd., 1952

CURIE, EVE; *Madame Curie, A Biography,* Doubleday & Co., 1951

CURIE, MARIE; *Pierre Curie,* Macmillan, 1923

DUNHAM, C. L.; Atomic Energy Activities of Medicine and Medical Research, *Rocky Mountain Medical Journal* 54: 23, Jan. 1957

EVE, A. S.; *Rutherford, Being the Life and Letters of Rt. Hon. Lord Rutherford,* Cambridge University Press, 1939

FERMI, LAURA; *Atoms in the Family: My Life.with Enrico Fermi, Architect of the Atomic Age,* University of Chicago Press, 1954

FRANK, PHILIPP; *Einstein, His Life and Times,* Alfred A. Knopf, 1953

FRISCH, O. R.; *Meet the Atom,* A. A. Wyn, 1947

GARBEDIAN, H. GORDON; *Albert Einstein, Maker of Universes,* Funk & Wagnalls Co., 1939

HARROW, BENJAMIN; *Eminent Chemists of our Time,* D. Van Nostrand Co., 1927

HAWLEY, G. G.; LEIFSON, S. W.; *Atomic Energy in War and Peace,* Reinhold Pub., 1945

HECHT, SELIG; *Explaining the Atom,* The Viking Press, 1947

HOPKINS, JOHN JAY; Unatom, A Plan for the Development of a United Atomic Treaty Organization of Free World Nations, An Address to the Third International Conference of Manufacturers, National Association of Manufacturers, Nov. 29, 1956

HOPKINS, JOHN JAY; *World Wide Industrial Role of Nuclear Energy,* General Dynamics Corporation, 1956

JAFFE, BERNARD; *Men of Science in America,* Simon & Schuster, 1944

KAPLAN, FLORA; *Nobel Prize Winners,* Nobelle Publishing Co., 1941

KRAUSKOPF, KONRAD; *Fundamentals of Physical Science,* 2nd ed., McGraw-Hill, 1948

KUGELMASS, J. ALVIN; *J. Robert Oppenheimer and the Atomic Story,* Messner, 1953

LAPP, RALPH, E.; *The New Force,* Harper & Bros., 1953

LAURENCE, WILLIAM L.; *Dawn Over Zero,* Alfred A. Knopf, 1946

RAYLEIGH, (LORD); *The Life of Sir J. J. Thomson,* Cambridge University Press, 1943

ROUZE, MICHEL; *Frédéric Joliot-Curie,* Les Editeurs Francais Reunis, 1950

RUSSELL, A. S.; F. Soddy, Interpreter of Atomic Structure, *Science,* 124 : 1069, Nov. 30, 1956

SMYTH, H. D.; *Atomic Energy for Military Purposes,* Princeton University Press, 1945

THOMSON, J. J.; *Recollections and Reflections,* The Macmillan Co., 1937

THOMSON, G.; J. J. Thomson, *Science* 124 : 1191, Dec. 14, 1956

TUTIN, J.; *Atomic Energy Year Book,* Prentice-Hall, Inc., 1949

INDEX